Prentice Hall
# Algebra 2

# Chapter 7
## Exponential and Logarithmic Functions

# All-In-One
# Teaching Resources

PEARSON

Boston, Massachusetts   Chandler, Arizona   Glenview, Illinois   Upper Saddle River, New Jersey

**PEARSON**

ISBN-13: 978-0-13-368936-5
ISBN-10:    0-13-368936-0

3 4 5 6 7 8 9 10  V084   13 12 11 10

# Contents

# 7-1  ELL Support

## Exploring Exponential Models

**Choose the word or phrase from the list that best completes each sentence.**

| | | |
|---|---|---|
| exponential function | exponential growth | exponential decay |
| asymptote | growth factor | decay factor |

1. In the function $y = 12(2.3)^x$, the value 2.3 is the _____.

2. An _____ is a line that a graph approaches as $x$ or $y$ increases in absolute value.

3. For _____, as the value of $x$ increases, the value of $y$ decreases.

4. A function in the general form $y = ab^x$ is called an _____.

5. For _____, as the value of $x$ increases, the value of $y$ increases.

6. In the function $y = 4(0.3)^x$, the value 0.3 is the _____.

**Identify whether each function represents exponential growth or exponential decay.**

7. $y = 0.75(4)^x$ _____

8. $y = 0.63(0.5)^x$ _____

9. $y = 9(0.83)^x$ _____

10. $y = 12(7)^x$ _____

**Identify the $y$-intercept for each function.**

11. $y = 4.5(7)^x$ _____

12. $y = 5(3.2)^x$ _____

**Prentice Hall Algebra 2** • Teaching Resources
1

# 7-1

## Think About a Plan

Exploring Exponential Models

**Population** The population of a certain animal species decreases at a rate of 3.5% per year. You have counted 80 of the animals in the habitat you are studying.

    **a.** Write a function that models the change in the animal population.

    **b. Graphing Calculator** Graph the function. Estimate the number of years until the population first drops below 15 animals.

**1.** Is an exponential model reasonable for this situation? Explain.

_____

_____ .

**2.** Write the function that models exponential growth or decay. $A(t) = $ ⬚

**3.** The initial population is ⬚ .

**4.** Is the rate of change positive or negative? Explain.

_____ .

**5.** The rate of change is ⬚ .

**6.** Write a function that models the change in the animal population. $P(t) = $ ⬚

**7.** Graph your function on a graphing calculator. Sketch your graph.

**8.** How can you find the $x$-value that produces a given $y$-value?

_____ .

**9.** Use your graph to estimate the number of years until the population first drops below 15 animals.

## 7-1 Practice                *Form G*

### Exploring Exponential Models

**Graph each function.**

**1.** $y = (0.3)^x$

**2.** $y = 3^x$

**3.** $y = 2\left(\frac{1}{5}\right)^x$

**4.** $y = \frac{1}{2}(3)^x$

**5.** $s(t) = 2.5^t$

**6.** $f(x) = \frac{1}{2}(5)^x$

**Without graphing, determine whether the function represents exponential growth or exponential decay. Then find the y-intercept.**

**7.** $y = 0.99\left(\frac{1}{3}\right)^x$

**8.** $y = 20(1.75)^x$

**9.** $y = 185\left(\frac{5}{4}\right)^x$

**10.** $f(x) = \frac{2}{3}\left(\frac{1}{2}\right)^x$

**11.** $f(x) = 0.25(1.05)^x$

**12.** $y = \frac{1}{5}\left(\frac{6}{5}\right)^x$

**13.** Suppose you deposit $1500 in a savings account that pays interest at an annual rate of 6%. No money is added or withdrawn from the account.
    **a.** How much will be in the account after 5 years?
    **b.** How much will be in the account after 20 years?
    **c.** How many years will it take for the account to contain $2500?
    **d.** How many years will it take for the account to contain $4000?

**Write an exponential function to model each situation. Find each amount after the specified time.**

**14.** A population of 1,236,000 grows 1.3% per year for 10 years.

**15.** A population of 752,000 decreases 1.4% per year for 18 years.

**16.** A new car that sells for $18,000 depreciates 25% each year for 4 years.

# 7-1

**Practice** (continued)                                                    Form G

Exploring Exponential Models

**For each annual rate of change, find the corresponding growth or decay factor.**

**17.** +45%          **18.** −10%          **19.** −40%          **20.** +200%

**21.** +28%          **22.** +100%         **23.** −5%           **24.** +3%

**25.** In 2009, there were 1570 bears in a wildlife refuge. In 2010, the population had increased to approximately 1884 bears. If this trend continues and the bear population is increasing exponentially, how many bears will there be in 2010?

**26.** The value of a piece of equipment has a decay factor of 0.80 per year. After 5 years, the equipment is worth $98,304. What was the original value of the equipment?

**27.** Your friend drops a rubber ball from 4 ft. You notice that its rebound is 32.5 in. on the first bounce and 22 in. on the second bounce.
   **a.** What exponential function would be a good model for the height of the ball?
   **b.** How high will the ball bounce on the fourth bounce?

**28.** An investment of $75,000 increases at a rate of 12.5% per year. What is the value of the investment after 30 years?

**29.** A new truck that sells for $29,000 depreciates 12% each year. What is the value of the truck after 7 years?

**30.** The price of a new home is $350,000. The value of the home appreciates 2% each year. How much will the home be worth in 10 years?

**31.** The population of an endangered bird is decreasing at a rate of 0.75% per year. There are currently about 200,000 of these birds.
   **a.** What exponential function would be a good model for the population of these endangered birds?
   **b.** How many birds will there be in 100 years?

# 7-1
## Practice
### Exploring Exponential Models

**Complete the table of values for each function. Then graph the function.**

**1.** $y = 3^x$

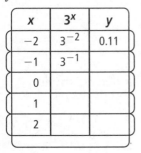

| x | $3^x$ | y |
|---|-------|---|
| −2 | $3^{-2}$ | 0.11 |
| −1 | $3^{-1}$ | |
| 0 | | |
| 1 | | |
| 2 | | |

**2.** $y = 0.5(2)^x$

| x | $0.5(2)^x$ | y |
|---|------------|---|
| −1 | $0.5(2)^{-1}$ | |
| 0 | | |
| 1 | | |
| 2 | | |
| 3 | | |
| 4 | | |

**3.** $y = 3(2)^x$

| x | $3(2)^x$ | y |
|---|----------|---|
| −2 | | |
| −1 | | |
| 0 | | |
| 1 | | |
| 2 | | |

**4.** $y = 2(0.5)^x$

| x | $2(0.5)^x$ | y |
|---|------------|---|
| −2 | | |
| −1 | | |
| 0 | | |
| 1 | | |
| 2 | | |

**Without graphing, determine whether the function represents exponential growth or exponential decay.**

**5.** $y = 3(7)^x$

**6.** $y = 4(2.5)^x$

**7.** $y = 5(0.75)^x$

**8.** $y = 0.5(0.2)^x$

**9.** $y = 10(6)^x$

**10.** $y = 0.6^x$

**Find the y-intercept of each function.**

**11.** $y = 2(0.75)^x$

**12.** $y = 0.75(3)^x$

**13.** $y = 3^x$

## 7-1 Practice (continued) Form K

### Exploring Exponential Models

**For each annual rate of change, find the corresponding growth or decay factor.**

**14.** 35%                    **15.** −20%                    **16.** 62%

**17.** Identify the meaning of the variables in the exponential growth or decay function.

$$A(t) = a(1 + r)^t$$

    **a.** $a = $ _____

    **b.** $r = $ _____

    **c.** $t = $ _____

**18.** The population of Bainsville is 2000. The population is supposed to grow by 10% each year for the next 5 years. How many people will live in Bainsville in 5 years?

**19. Writing** Describe a situation that could be modeled by the function $A(t) = 200(1.05)^x$.

**20.** A music store sold 200 guitars in 2007. The store sold 180 guitars in 2008. The number of guitars that the store sells is decreasing exponentially. If this trend continues, how many guitars will the store sell in 2012?

$r = \dfrac{y_2 - y_1}{y_1}$            $A(t) = a(1 + r)^t$

$r = \dfrac{180 - 200}{200}$            $A(5) = $

$r = $

# 7-1

## Standardized Test Prep

Exploring Exponential Models

## Multiple Choice

**For Exercises 1 and 2, choose the correct letter.**

1. Which of the following functions represents exponential decay and has a
   $y$-intercept of 2?

   Ⓐ $y = 2\left(\frac{4}{3}\right)^x$          Ⓒ $y = \frac{1}{4}(2)^x$

   Ⓑ $y = \frac{1}{2}(0.95)^x$          Ⓓ $y = 2\left(\frac{2}{5}\right)^x$

2. Suppose you deposit $3000 in a savings account that pays interest at an annual
   rate of 4%. If no other money is added or withdrawn from the account, how
   much will be in the account after 10 years?

   Ⓕ $3122.18          Ⓗ $4440.73

   Ⓖ $4994.50          Ⓘ $86,776.40

## Extended Response

3. In 2009 there was an endangered population of 270 cranes in a western state.
   Due to wildlife efforts, the population is increasing at a rate of 5% per year.
   a. What exponential function would be a good model for this population
      of cranes? Explain in words or show work for how you determined the
      exponential function.
   b. If this trend continues, how many cranes will there be in this population in
      2020? Show your work.

# 7-1 Enrichment

## Exploring Exponential Models

### Determining Relationships Between Variables

On the basis of data, scientists sometimes hypothesize that a quantity $z$ depends on two quantities $x$ and $y$ such that

$$z = Cx^ry^s$$

where $C$ is a constant and $r$ and $s$ are integers. By doing experiments in which the values of $x$ and $y$ are varied, they determine the values of integers $r$ and $s$.

For instance, suppose the momentum $M$ of a moving object seems to be related to the mass $m$ and velocity $v$ by the equation $M = Cm^rv^s$. Later, scientists find that doubling the mass and keeping the velocity constant doubles the momentum, so

$$2M = C(2m)^rv^s.$$

Using substitution and simplifying: $\quad\quad 2(Cm^rv^s) = C2^rm^rv^s$

Dividing each side by $Cm^rv^s$: $\quad\quad\quad\quad\quad 2 = 2^r$

$$1 = r$$

1. Suppose that doubling the velocity while holding the mass constant also doubles the momentum. Express this relationship in an equation.

2. Solve your equation for $s$.

3. Use the values of $r$ and $s$ to write an expression for momentum in terms of mass $m$, velocity $v$, and the constant $C$.

**Use a similar method to solve the following problems.**

4. The price $P$ of a diamond is related to both the weight $W$ of the diamond and its brilliance $B$. If both the weight and brilliance are simultaneously doubled, the price of the diamond increases by a factor of 32. If the weight is doubled and, at the same time, the brilliance is halved, the price increases by a factor of 2. Write a formula for $P$ in terms of $W$, $B$, and the constant $C$.

5. The price of wheat depends upon the weight and the water content. A particular wheat trader pays according to this pattern: the price $P$ increases by a factor of 2 when the weight is doubled and the water content is constant. If the weight is doubled and the water content is halved, the price is constant. Write a formula for $P$ in terms of weight $w$, water content $h$, and the constant $C$.

# 7-1 Reteaching

## Exploring Exponential Models

- The general form of an exponential function is $y = ab^x$, where $a$ is the initial amount and $b$ is the growth or decay factor.

- To find $b$, use the formula $b = 1 + r$, where $r$ is the constant rate of growth or decay. If $r$ is a rate of growth, it will be positive. If $r$ is a rate of decay, it will be negative. Therefore, if $b$ is greater than 1, the function models growth. If $b$ is between zero and 1, the function models decay. When you see words like *increase* or *appreciation*, think growth. When you see words like *decrease* or *depreciation*, think decay.

- For an exponential function, the $y$-intercept is always equal to the value of $a$.

### Problem

Carl's weight at 12 yr is 82 lb. Assume that his weight increases at a rate of 16% each year. Write an exponential function to model the increase. What is his weight after 5 years?

**Step 1** Find $a$ and $b$.

$a = 82$        $a$ is the original amount.

$b = 1 + 0.16$        $b$ is the growth or decay factor. Since this problem models growth, $r$ will be positive. Make sure to rewrite the rate, $r$, as a decimal.

$= 1.16$

**Step 2** Write the exponential function.

$y = ab^x$        Use the formula.

$y = 82(1.16)^x$        Substitute.

**Step 3** Calculate.

$y = 82(1.16)^5$        Substitute 5 for $x$.

$y \approx 172.228$        Use a calculator.

Carl will weigh about 172 lb in 5 years.

## Exercises

**Determine whether the function represents exponential growth or exponential decay. Then find the $y$-intercept.**

**1.** $y = 8000(1.15)^x$                **2.** $y = 20(0.75)^x$

**3.** $y = 15\left(\frac{1}{2}\right)^x$                **4.** $f(x) = 6\left(\frac{5}{2}\right)^x$

Name _____  Class _____  Date _____

# 7-1 **Reteaching** (continued)
## Exploring Exponential Models

You can use the general form of an exponential function to solve word problems involving growth or decay.

**Problem**

A motorcycle purchased for $9000 today will be worth 6% less each year. How much will the motorcycle be worth at the end of 5 years?

**Step 1** Find $a$ and $b$.

$a = 9000$      $a$ is the original amount.

$b = 1 + (-0.06)$      $b$ is the growth or decay factor. Since this problem models decay, $r$ will be negative. Make sure to rewrite the rate, $r$, as a decimal.

$= 0.94$

**Step 2** Write the exponential function.

$y = ab^x$      Use the formula.

$y = 9000(0.94)^x$      Substitute.

**Step 3** Calculate.

$y = 9000(0.94)^5$      Substitute 5 for $x$.

$y \approx 6605.13$      Use a calculator.

The motorcycle will be worth about $6605.13 after 5 years.

## Exercises

**Write an exponential function to model each situation. Find each amount after the specified time.**

5. A tree 3 ft tall grows 8% each year. How tall will the tree be at the end of 14 yr? Round the answer to the nearest hundredth.

6. The price of a new home is $126,000. The value of the home appreciates 2% each year. How much will the home be worth in 10 yr?

7. A butterfly population is decreasing at a rate of 0.82% per year. There are currently about 100,000 butterflies in the population. How many butterflies will there be in the population in 250 years?

8. A car depreciates 10% each year. If you bought this car today for $5000, how much will it be worth in 7 years?

# 7-2  ELL Support

Properties of Exponential Functions

**Concept List**

| | |
|---|---|
| compression | continuously compounded interest |
| horizontal translation 3 units to the right | natural base exponential function |
| parent function | reflection in *x*-axis |
| stretch | vertical translation 3 units upward |

Choose the concept from the list above that best represents the item in each box.

| | |
|---|---|
| **1.** $y = 3 \cdot 5^x$ | **2.** $y = 0.67^x$ |
| **3.** $y = 7^x + 3$ | **4.** $A(t) = P \cdot e^{rt}$ |
| **5.** $y = -7^x$ | **6.** $y = 0.56(7)^x$ |
| **7.** $y = e^5$ | **8.** $y = 11^{(x-3)}$ |

# 7-2   Think About a Plan

Properties of Exponential Functions

**Investment**  How long would it take to double your principal in an account that pays 6.5% annual interest compounded continuously?

## Know

1. The equation for continuously compounded interest is [          ].

2. The principal is [        ].

3. The interest rate is [        ].

## Need

4. To solve the problem I need to:

   _____ .

## Plan

5. If the principal is $P$, then twice the principal is [        ].

6. What equation can you use to find the time it takes to double your principal?

7. Solve your equation for $t$.

8. Is your solution reasonable? Explain.

   _____

   _____ .

# 7-2 | **Practice** | Form G

Properties of Exponential Functions

**Graph each function.**

**1.** $y = 2^x$

**2.** $y = 5(0.12)^x$

**3.** $y = 5^x$

**4.** $y = -0.1(5)^x$

**5.** $y = \left(\frac{1}{5}\right)^x$

**6.** $y = -5\left(\frac{1}{3}\right)^x$

**Graph each function as a transformation of its parent function.**

**7.** $y = 2^{x+1}$

**8.** $y = -(2)^{x+1}$

**9.** $y = 5^{-x}$

**10.** $y = -0.1(5)^{-x}$

**11.** $y = 2(2)^{x+2}$

**12.** $y = 2^x + 1$

**13.** A cake is 190°F when you remove it from the oven. You must let it cool to 75°F before you can frost it. The table at the right shows the temperature readings for the cake.

   **a.** Given a room temperature of 68°F, what is an exponential model for this data set?

   **b.** How long must the cake cool before you can frost it?

| Time (min) | Temp (°F) |
|------------|-----------|
| 0          | 190       |
| 5          | 149       |
| 10         | 122       |
| 15         | 104       |
| 20         | 92        |

**Use the graph of $y = e^x$ to evaluate each expression to four decimal places.**

**14.** $e^2$

**15.** $e^{-2.5}$

**16.** $e^{\frac{1}{3}}$

## 7-2 Practice (continued)        Form G
Properties of Exponential Functions

**Find the amount in a continuously compounded account for the given conditions.**

**17.** principal: $5000
    annual interest rate: 6.9%
    time: 30 yr

**18.** principal: $20,000
    annual interest rate: 3.75%
    time: 2 yr

**19.** How long would it take to double your principal at an annual interest rate of 7% compounded continuously?

**20. Error Analysis** A student says that the graph of $f(x) = 2^{x+3} + 4$ is a shift of 3 units up and 4 units to the right of the parent function. Describe and correct the student's error.

**21.** The isotope Hg-197 is used in kidney scans. It has a half-life of 64.128 h. After that time, half the isotope will have decayed. Write the exponential decay function for a 12-mg sample. Find the amount remaining after 72 h.

**22.** The isotope Sr-85 is used in bone scans. It has a half-life of 64.9 days. Write the exponential decay function for an 8-mg sample. Find the amount remaining after 100 days.

**23.** Suppose you invest $2000 at an annual interest of 5.5% compounded continuously.
    **a.** How much will you have in the account in 10 years?
    **b.** How long will it take for the account to reach $5000?

**The parent function for each graph below is of the form $y = ab^x$. Write the parent function. Then write a function for the translation indicated.**

**24.**
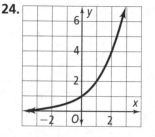
translation: left 3 units, up 1 unit

**25.**
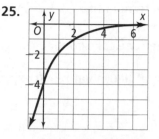
translation: right 2 units, up 3 units

# 7-2 **Practice** Form K

## Properties of Exponential Functions

**Write the parent function of each function.**

**1.** $y = 5 \cdot 3^x$

**2.** $y = 7^{(x-3)}$

**3.** $y = 6^{(x-2)} + 9$

**Graph each of the following functions.**

**4.** $y = 4^x$

**5.** $y = 0.5 \cdot 2^x$

**Identify each function as a compression, a reflection, or a translation of the parent function.**

**6.**
**7.**
**8.**

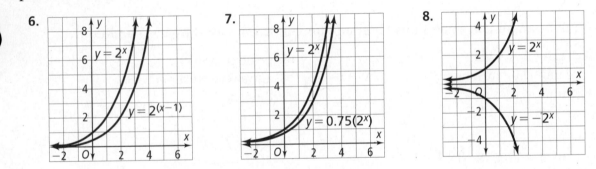

**Write a function for the indicated transformation.**

**9.** the function $y = 5^{(x-2)}$ vertically stretched by the factor 3

**10.** the function $y = 7 \cdot 2^x$ translated up 8 units

## 7-2 **Practice** (continued)          Form K

Properties of Exponential Functions

Use the graph of $y = e^x$ to evaluate each expression to four decimal places.

**11.** $e^3$                          **12.** $e^{0.5}$                         **13.** $e^{-4}$

Identify the meaning of the following variables in the formula for continuously compounded interest.

$$A(t) = P \cdot e^{rt}$$

**14.** $P$                         **15.** $r$                             **16.** $t$

Find the amount in a continuously compounded account for the given conditions.

**17.** principal: $300
annual interest rate: 5%
time: 4 yr

$A(t) = P \cdot e^{rt}$
$A(4) = \$300 \cdot e^{(0.05)(4)}$
$A(4) =$

**18.** principal: $650
annual interest rate: 6.5%
time: 20 yr

$A(t) = P \cdot e^{rt}$
$A(t) =$

**19.** Sarah received a paycheck for $1200. She deposited $\frac{1}{4}$ of the money into a bank account. The account has an interest rate of 6% compounded continuously. This is the first and last deposit that Sarah makes into this account. How much money will be in the account in 15 years?

# 7-2 Standardized Test Prep

Properties of Exponential Functions

## Gridded Response

**Solve each exercise and enter your answer in the grid provided.**

1. Suppose you deposit $6000 in a savings account that pays interest at an annual rate of 4% compounded continuously. How many years will it take for the balance in your savings account to reach $8000? Round your answer up to the nearest number of years.

2. Suppose you make $1500 at your summer job and you decide to invest this money in a savings account that pays interest at an annual rate of 5.5% compounded continuously. How many dollars will be in the account after 5 years? Express the answer to the nearest whole dollar.

3. The half-life of a radioactive substance is the time it takes for half of the material to decay. Phosphorus-32 is used to study a plant's use of fertilizer. It has a half-life of 14.3 days. How many milligrams of phosphorus-32 remain after 92 days from a 100-mg sample? Express the answer to the nearest whole milligram.

4. A scientist notes the bacteria count in a petrie dish is 40. Three hours later, she notes the count has increased to 75. Using an exponential model, how many hours will it take for the bacteria count to grow from 75 to 120? Express the answer to the nearest tenth of an hour.

## Answers

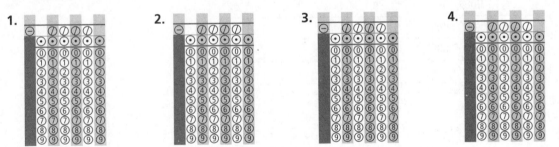

1.   2.   3.   4.

**Prentice Hall Algebra 2** • Teaching Resources

**17**

# 7-2 Enrichment

## Properties of Exponential Functions

## A Closer Look at Compounding

The formula for finding the amount of money accumulated in an account is

$A = P(1 + \frac{r}{n})^{nt}$.

The variable **P** represents the **principal**, or amount initially invested.
The variable **r** represents the interest **rate** as a decimal.
The variable **n** represents the number of times per year the interest is **compounded**.
The variable **t** represents the **time**, or number of years for which the money is invested.

1. $750 is invested at 11% compounded quarterly. How much is in the account after 10 yr?

2. Write the new formula for $P = \$1, r = 1.0$, and $t = 1$ yr.

3. Remember that *n* is the number of times the interest is compounded. What happens as *n* grows? In other words, what is the effect of compounding more often? Fill in the following table. Round answers to eight decimal places.

| $n$ | $\left(1 + \frac{1}{n}\right)^n$ |
|---|---|
| 1 | |
| 10 | |
| 100 | |
| 1,000 | |
| 10,000 | |
| 100,000 | |
| 1,000,000 | |
| 10,000,000 | |
| 100,000,000 | |
| 1,000,000,000 | |

4. The table suggests that as *n* increases, the value of $\left(1 + \frac{1}{n}\right)^n$ gets closer to [____]. If the value of *n* is increased further, the decimal approximation in the table will get very close to the value of a number known as *e*. This number is used in many growth and decay applications.

5. As *n* grows, you get closer to compounding continuously. This is why the formula used for compounding continuously is $A = Pe^{rt}$. Rework Exercise 1 assuming that compounding is continuous.

# 7-2 Reteaching

Properties of Exponential Functions

There are four types of transformations that can change the graph of an exponential function.

### Stretches

The factor $a$ in $y = ab^x$ can stretch the graph of an exponential function when

$$|a| > 1$$

### Compressions

The factor $a$ in $y = ab^x$ can compress the graph of an exponential function when

$$0 < |a| < 1$$

### Reflections

The factor $a$ in $y = ab^x$ can reflect the graph of an exponential function in the $x$-axis when

$$a < 0$$

### Translations

The graph of an exponential function translates horizontally by $h$; vertically by $k$.

$$y = ab^{(x-h)} + k$$

**Problem**

How does the graph of $y = 2\left(\frac{1}{3}\right)^{x+1} - 4$ compare to the parent function $y = 2\left(\frac{1}{3}\right)^x$?

**Step 1** Determine the base of the function $y = 2\left(\frac{1}{3}\right)^x$. Because $b < 1$, the graph will represent exponential decay.

**Step 2** Make a table. Find more values if necessary to get a good picture of the graph.

**Step 3** Use the values for $x$ and $y$ from the table to graph the function.

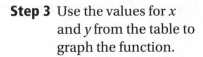

| $x$ | $y = 2\left(\frac{1}{3}\right)^x$ | $y$ |
|---|---|---|
| $-2$ | $2\left(\frac{1}{3}\right)^{-2} = 2(9)$ | $18$ |
| $-1$ | $2\left(\frac{1}{3}\right)^{-1} = 2(3)$ | $6$ |
| $0$ | $2\left(\frac{1}{3}\right)^{0} = 2(1)$ | $2$ |
| $1$ | $2\left(\frac{1}{3}\right)^{1} = 2\left(\frac{1}{3}\right)$ | $\frac{2}{3}$ |
| $2$ | $2\left(\frac{1}{3}\right)^{2} = 2\left(\frac{1}{9}\right)$ | $\frac{2}{9}$ |

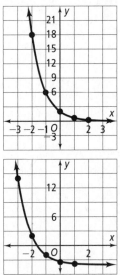

**Step 4** For $y = 2\left(\frac{1}{3}\right)^{x+1} - 4$, $h = -1$ and $k = -4$. Shift the graph of the parent function above 1 unit left and 4 units down. The horizontal asymptote shifts down as well, from $y = 0$ to $y = -4$.

**Step 5** Use a graphing calculator to check your graph.

**Prentice Hall Algebra 2 • Teaching Resources**

# 7-2 Reteaching (continued)
## Properties of Exponential Functions

For problems involving continuously compounded interest, use the following formula:

*Continuously Compounded Interest*   $A(t)$ is the amount in account after time $t$.

$$A(t) = P \cdot e^{rt}$$

$P$ is the principal.

$r$ is the annual interest rate (as a decimal).

$t$ is time (in years).

### Problem

Suppose you invest $2000 at an annual interest rate of 5.5% compounded continuously. How much will you have in the account in 10 years?

**What do you know?**

principal $P = \$2000$
interest rate $r = 5.5\% = 0.055$
time $t = 10$ years

**Use the formula.**

$A(t) = P \cdot e^{rt}$
$\quad = 2000 \cdot e^{(0.055)(10)}$
$\quad = 2000 \cdot e^{0.55}$
$\quad \approx 3466.50$

In ten years, you will have $3466.50.

## Exercises

**Graph each exponential function.**

**1.** $y = \left(\frac{1}{5}\right)^x$

**2.** $y = 3^x + 1$

**3.** $y = 5^x$

**4.** $y = -\left(\frac{1}{2}\right)^x$

**5.** $y = -\left(\frac{1}{2}\right)^x + 4$

**6.** $y = \left(\frac{1}{4}\right)^x$

**7.** $y = \left(\frac{1}{4}\right)^{x-1}$

**8.** $y = 4^x + 1$

**9.** $y = -(2)^x$

**10.** Suppose you invest $7500 at an annual interest of 7% compounded continuously.
   **a.** How much will you have in the account in 10 years?
   **b.** How long will it take for the account to reach $20,000?

# 7-3 ELL Support

## Logarithmic Functions as Inverses

**For Exercises 1–3, draw a line from each word or phrase in Column A to the matching item in Column B.**

| Column A | Column B |
|---|---|
| **1.** logarithmic function | **A.** a logarithm with base 10 |
| **2.** common logarithm | **B.** the inverse of an exponential function |
| **3.** logarithmic scale | **C.** uses the logarithm of a quantity instead of the quantity itself |

**For Exercises 4–9, draw a line from each word or phrase in Column A to the matching item in Column B.**

| Column A | Column B |
|---|---|
| **4.** parent function | **A.** $y = 0.75 \log_4 x$ |
| **5.** stretch | **B.** $y = 5 \log_4 x$ |
| **6.** compression | **C.** $y = \log_4 x - 3$ |
| **7.** reflection in $x$-axis | **D.** $y = \log_4 x$ |
| **8.** translation 3 units to the right | **E.** $y = -\log_4 x$ |
| **9.** translation 3 units downward | **F.** $y = \log_4 (x - 3)$ |

# 7-3 Think About a Plan

Logarithmic Functions as Inverses

**Chemistry** Find the concentration of hydrogen ions in seawater, if the pH level of seawater is 8.5.

## Understanding the Problem

1. What is the pH of seawater?

2. How do you represent the concentration of hydrogen ions?

3. What is the problem asking you to determine?

## Planning the Solution

4. Write the formula for the pH of a substance.

5. Write an equation relating the pH of seawater to the concentration of hydrogen ions in seawater.

## Getting an Answer

6. Solve your equation to find the concentration of hydrogen ions in seawater.

# 7-3    **Practice**                      *Form G*

Logarithmic Functions as Inverses

**Write each equation in logarithmic form.**

**1.** $9^2 = 81$         **2.** $\frac{1}{64} = \left(\frac{1}{4}\right)^3$       **3.** $8^3 = 512$       **4.** $\left(\frac{1}{3}\right)^{-2} = 9$

**5.** $2^9 = 512$       **6.** $4^5 = 1024$       **7.** $5^4 = 625$       **8.** $10^{23} = 0.001$

**Evaluate each logarithm.**

**9.** $\log_2 128$       **10.** $\log_4 32$       **11.** $\log_9 (27)$       **12.** $\log_2 (-32)$

**13.** $\log_{\frac{1}{3}} \frac{1}{9}$       **14.** $\log 100{,}000$       **15.** $\log_7 7^6$       **16.** $\log_3 \frac{1}{81}$

**In 2004, an earthquake of magnitude 7.0 shook Papua, Indonesia. Compare the intensity level of that earthquake to the intensity level of each earthquake below.**

**17.** magnitude 6.1 in Costa Rica, in 2009

**18.** magnitude 5.1 in Greece, in 2008

**19.** magnitude 7.8 in the Fiji Islands, in 2007

**20.** magnitude 8.3 in the Kuril Islands, in 2006

**Graph each logarithmic function.**

**21.** $y = \log x$           **22.** $y = \log_3 x$           **23.** $y = \log_6 x$

# 7-3 Practice (continued) Form G

Logarithmic Functions as Inverses

**Describe how the graph of each function compares with the graph of the parent function, $y = \log_b x$.**

**24.** $y = \log_3 x - 2$

**25.** $y = \log_8 (x - 2)$

**26.** $y = \log_6 (x + 1) - 5$

**27.** $y = \log_2 (x - 4) + 1$

**Write each equation in exponential form.**

**28.** $\log_4 256 = 4$ **29.** $\log_7 1 = 0$ **30.** $\log_2 32 = 5$

**31.** $\log 10 = 1$ **32.** $\log_5 5 = 1$ **33.** $\log_8 \frac{1}{64} = -2$

**34.** $\log_9 59{,}049 = 5$ **35.** $\log_{17} 289 = 2$ **36.** $\log_{56} 1 = 0$

**37.** $\log_{12} \frac{1}{144} = -2$ **38.** $\log_2 \frac{1}{1024} = -10$ **39.** $\log_3 6561 = 8$

**40.** A single-celled bacterium divides every hour. The number $N$ of bacteria after $t$ hours is given by the formula $\log_2 N = t$. After how many hours will there be 32 bacteria?

**For each pH given, find the concentration of hydrogen ions $[H^+]$. Use the formula $pH = -\log[H^+]$.**

**41.** 7.2 **42.** 7.3 **43.** 8.2 **44.** 6.2

**45.** 5.6 **46.** 4.6 **47.** 7.0 **48.** 2.9

**Find the inverse of each function.**

**49.** $y = \log_2 x$ **50.** $y = \log_{0.7} x$ **51.** $y = \log_{100} x$

**52.** $y = \log_8 x$ **53.** $y = \log_2 (4x)$ **54.** $y = \log (x + 4)$

**Find the domain and range of each function.**

**55.** $y = \log_3 x - 2$ **56.** $y = 2\log_5 x$ **57.** $y = \log (x + 1)$

## 7-3 Practice
Form K

Logarithmic Functions as Inverses

**Write each equation in logarithmic form.**

**1.** $32 = 2^5$

**2.** $243 = 3^5$

**3.** $625 = 5^4$

**Write each equation in exponential form.**

**4.** $\log_3 9 = 2$

**5.** $\log_5 125 = 3$

**6.** $\log_8 512 = 3$

**Evaluate each logarithm.**

**7.** $\log_9 27$

$\log_9 27 = x$

$27 = 9^x$

$3^3 = \left(3^2\right)^x$

$3^3 = 3^{2x}$

$3 = 2x$

$x =$

**8.** $\log_8 256$

$\log_8 256 = x$

$256 = 8^x$

**9.** $\log_{125} \frac{1}{25}$

The formula $\log \frac{I_1}{I_2} = M_1 - M_2$ is used to compare the intensity levels of earthquakes. The variable $I$ is the intensity measured by a seismograph. The variable $M$ is the measurement on the Richter scale. Use the formula to answer the following problem.

**10.** In 1906, an earthquake of magnitude 8.25 hit San Francisco, California. Indonesia was hit by an earthquake of magnitude 8.5 in 1938. Compare the intensity of the two earthquakes.

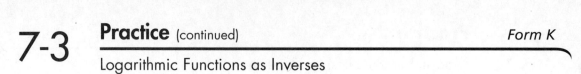

**7-3** **Practice** (continued)        Form K

Logarithmic Functions as Inverses

**11. Error Analysis** A student drew the graph below to represent the function $y = \log_4 x$. What mistake did the student make when she drew her graph?

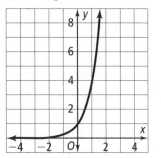

**Graph each logarithmic function.**

**12.** $y = \log_2 x$                              **13.** $y = \log_{\frac{1}{3}} x$

**Identify each function as a compression, a stretch, or a translation of the parent function.**

**14.** $y = 4 \log_3 x$          **15.** $y = \log_2 x + 10$          **16.** $y = 0.25 \log_4 x$

**Transform the function $y = \log_5 x$ as indicated below.**

**17.** stretch by a factor of 3 and translate 6 units up

**18.** compress by a factor of 0.4 and reflect in the $x$-axis

# 7-3 Standardized Test Prep

Logarithmic Functions as Inverses

## Multiple Choice

**For Exercises 1–4, choose the correct letter.**

1. Which of the following is the logarithmic form of the equation $4^{-3} = \frac{1}{64}$?

   (A) $\log_{-3}\left(\frac{1}{64}\right) = 4$           (C) $\log_4\left(\frac{1}{64}\right) = -3$

   (B) $\log_{-3} 4 = \frac{1}{64}$             (D) $\log_{\frac{1}{64}} 4 = -3$

2. What is the value of $\log_2 8$?

   (F) 64                   (H) 16

   (G) 8                    (I) 3

3. How does the graph of $y = \log_5 (x - 3)$ compare with the graph of the parent function, $y = \log_5 x$?

   (A) translated 3 units to the left      (C) translated 3 units to the right

   (B) translated 3 units down         (D) translated 3 units up

4. In 2009, an earthquake of magnitude 6.7 shook the Kermadec Islands off the coast of New Zealand. Also in 2009, an earthquake of magnitude 5.1 occurred in the Alaska Peninsula. How many times stronger was the Kermadec earthquake than the Alaska earthquake?

   (F) 39.811               (H) 5.77

   (G) 20.593              (I) 0.025

## Short Response

5. A single-celled bacterium divides every hour. The number $N$ of bacteria after $t$ hours is given by the formula $\log_2 N = t$.
   a. After how many hours will there be 64 bacteria?
   b. Explain in words or show work for how you determined the number of hours.

## 7-3 Enrichment

Logarithmic Functions as Inverses

### Log Jams

The logarithm is a tool originally developed and used to aid in calculations, yet this viewpoint of logarithms is not the only one of interest. Logarithms are also useful when thought of as real-valued functions, or as inverse functions of the corresponding exponential functions. The idea of a logarithm as an inverse function of an exponential function means that $\log_b x$ is a question to be answered. For example, you can read the expression $\log_2 8$ as "what exponent on base 2 gives 8?" The answer is 3, because $2^3 = 8$.

Thinking of a logarithm as an exponent helps to order some logarithms without evaluating them. For example, the logarithms $\log_7 8$, $\log_7 7$, and $\log_7 6$ are in descending order since the exponent needed on base 7 that gives 8 would be greater than 1, and 1 is in turn greater than the exponent needed on base 7 that gives 6.

You can also compose logarithms as you would compose other functions, where their domain and ranges agree. Thus, you evaluate $\log_4 (\log_5 25)$ by evaluating $\log_5 25 = 2$, then evaluating $\log_4 2 = \frac{1}{2}$.

**Rewrite each equation in exponential form to solve the equation.**

**1.** Solve for $x$:   $\log_x 81 = 4$

**2.** Solve for $x$:   $\log_x 2 = 2$

**3.** Which is greater, $\log_2 3$ or $\log_3 2$?

**4.** Solve for $x$:   $\log_3 x = \log_x 3$

**5.** Which is greater, $\frac{1}{3}$ of $\log_4 2$ or $\frac{1}{2}$ of $\log 10$?

**6.** Solve for $x$:   $\log_2 (\log_2 x) = 2$

**7.** Which is greater, $\frac{1}{3} \log_2 (\log_3 8.5)$ or $\frac{1}{2} \log_3 (\log_2 8.5)$?

**8.** Which of the following are equal?

$\log \frac{1}{2}$  $\qquad\qquad$  $\dfrac{\log 1}{\log 2}$  $\qquad\qquad$  $\log 1 - \log 2$

**Rewrite in exponential form and solve for $x$.**

**9.** $\log_5 1 = x$ $\qquad\qquad\qquad$ **10.** $\log_2 (2x^2 - 7) = 0$

**11.** $\log_x 7 = 1$ $\qquad\qquad\qquad$ **12.** $\log_2 x^2 = 2$

**13.** $\log_3 1 = x$ $\qquad\qquad\qquad$ **14.** $\log_{17} 17 = x$

**15.** $\log_x 3^4 = 1$ $\qquad\qquad\qquad$ **16.** $\log_3 x = 0$

**17.** $\log_3 3^2 = x$ $\qquad\qquad\qquad$ **18.** $\log_4 (x + 1) = 0$

**19.** $1 + \log_6 (x - 1) = 1$ $\qquad\qquad$ **20.** $-1 + \log x = -1$

# 7-3 Reteaching
### Logarithmic Functions as Inverses

A logarithmic function is the inverse of an exponential function.

To evaluate logarithmic expressions, use the fact that $x = \log_b y$ is the same as $y = b^x$. Keep in mind that $x = \log y$ is another way of writing $x = \log_{10} y$.

**Problem**

What is the logarithmic form of $6^3 = 216$?

**Step 1** Determine which equation to use.

The equation is in the form $b^x = y$.

**Step 2** Find $x$, $y$, and $b$.

$b = 6$, $x = 3$, and $y = 216$

**Step 3** Because $y = b^x$ is the same as $x = \log_b y$, rewrite the equation in logarithmic form by substituting for $x$, $y$, and $b$.

$3 = \log_6 216$

## Exercises

**Write each equation in logarithmic form.**

**1.** $4^{-3} = \frac{1}{64}$    **2.** $5^{-2} = \frac{1}{25}$    **3.** $8^{-1} = \frac{1}{8}$    **4.** $11^0 = 1$

**5.** $6^1 = 6$    **6.** $6^{-3} = \frac{1}{216}$    **7.** $17^0 = 1$    **8.** $17^1 = 17$

**Problem**

What is the exponential form of $4 = \log_5 625$?

**Step 1** Determine which equation to use.

The equation is in the form $x = \log_b y$.

**Step 2** Find $x$, $y$, and $b$.

$x = 4$, $b = 5$, and $y = 625$

**Step 3** Because $x = \log_b y$ is the same as $y = b^x$, rewrite the equation in exponential form by substituting for $x$, $y$, and $b$.

$625 = 5^4$

## 7-3   Reteaching (continued)

Logarithmic Functions as Inverses

## Exercises

**Write each equation in exponential form.**

**9.** $3 = \log_2 8$

**10.** $2 = \log_5 25$

**11.** $\log 0.1 = -1$

**12.** $\log 7 \approx 0.845$

**13.** $\log 1000 = 3$

**14.** $-2 = \log 0.01$

**15.** $\log_3 81 = 4$

**16.** $\log_{49} 7 = \frac{1}{2}$

**17.** $\log_8 \frac{1}{4} = -\frac{2}{3}$

**18.** $\log_2 128 = 7$

**19.** $\log_5 \frac{1}{625} = -4$

**20.** $\log_6 36 = 2$

### Problem

What is the value of $\log_4 32$?

$x = \log_4 32$    Write the equation in logarithmic form $x = \log_b y$.

$32 = 4^x$    Rewrite in exponential form $y = b^x$.

$2^5 = (2^2)^x$    Rewrite each side of the equation with like bases in order to solve the equation.

$2^5 = 2^{2x}$    Simplify.

$5 = 2x$    Set the exponents equal to each other.

$x = \frac{5}{2}$    Solve for $x$.

$\log_4 32 = \frac{5}{2}$

## Exercises

**Evaluate the logarithm.**

**21.** $\log_2 64$

**22.** $\log_4 64$

**23.** $\log_3 3^4$

**24.** $\log 10$

**25.** $\log 0.1$

**26.** $\log 1$

**27.** $\log_8 2$

**28.** $\log_{32} 2$

**29.** $\log_9 3$

## 7-4 ELL Support
### Properties of Logarithms

| Product Property | Quotient Property | Power Property |
|---|---|---|
| $\log_b mn = \log_b m + \log_b n$ | $\log_b \frac{m}{n} = \log_b m - \log_b n$ | $\log_b m^n = n \log_b m$ |
| **Example:** | **Example:** | **Example:** |
| $\log_4 (4 \cdot 3) = \log_4 4 + \log_4 3$ | $\log_3 \frac{12}{5} = \log_3 12 - \log_3 5$ | $\log_5 7^3 = 3 \log_5 7$ |

**Identify the property that is demonstrated by each equation.**

**1.** $\log_4 \frac{7}{3} = \log_4 7 - \log_4 3$ _____

**2.** $\log_3 6^5 = 5 \log_3 6$ _____

**3.** $\log_7 \frac{15}{4} = \log_7 15 - \log_7 4$ _____

**4.** $\log_5 (6 \cdot 4) = \log_5 6 + \log_5 4$ _____

**5.** $\log_4 12^5 = 5 \log_4 12$ _____

**Identify the values of the symbols in the equations below.**

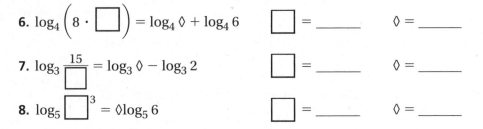

**6.** $\log_4 \left( 8 \cdot \square \right) = \log_4 \Diamond + \log_4 6$ $\quad \square =$ _____ $\quad \Diamond =$ _____

**7.** $\log_3 \dfrac{15}{\square} = \log_3 \Diamond - \log_3 2$ $\quad \square =$ _____ $\quad \Diamond =$ _____

**8.** $\log_5 \square^3 = \Diamond \log_5 6$ $\quad \square =$ _____ $\quad \Diamond =$ _____

**Write each expression as a single logarithm.**

**9.** $\log_8 6 - \log_8 2 =$ _____

**10.** $\log_6 5 + \log_6 3 =$ _____

# 7-4

## Think About a Plan

Properties of Logarithms

**Construction** The foreman of a construction team puts up a sound barrier that reduces the intensity of the noise by 50%. By how many decibels is the noise reduced? Use the formula $L = 10 \log \frac{I}{I_0}$ to measure loudness. (*Hint*: Find the difference between the expression for loudness for intensity $I$ and the expression for loudness for intensity $0.5I$.)

### Know

1. You can represent the intensity of the original noise by [           ].

2. You can represent the intensity of the reduced noise by [           ].

3. The formula for loudness is [                    ].

### Need

4. To solve the problem I need to find:

   _____

   _____.

### Plan

5. What is an expression for the loudness of the original construction noise?

6. What is an expression for the loudness of the reduced construction noise?

7. Use your expressions to find the difference between the loudness of the original construction noise and the loudness of the reduced construction noise.

8. The sound barrier reduced the loudness by [           ].

# 7-4  Practice                                           Form G
## Properties of Logarithms

**Write each expression as a single logarithm.**

**1.** $\log_5 4 + \log_5 3$

**2.** $\log_6 25 - \log_6 5$

**3.** $\log_2 4 + \log_2 2 - \log_2 8$

**4.** $5\log_7 x - 2\log_7 x$

**5.** $\log_4 60 - \log_4 4 + \log_4 x$

**6.** $\log 7 - \log 3 + \log 6$

**7.** $2\log x - 3\log y$

**8.** $\frac{1}{2}\log r + \frac{1}{3}\log s - \frac{1}{4}\log t$

**9.** $\log_3 4x + 2\log_3 5y$

**10.** $5\log 2 - 2\log 2$

**11.** $\frac{1}{3}\log 3x + \frac{2}{3}\log 3x$

**12.** $2\log 4 + \log 2 + \log 2$

**13.** $(\log 3 - \log 4) - \log 2$

**14.** $5\log x + 3\log x^2$

**15.** $\log_6 3 - \log_6 6$

**16.** $\log 2 + \log 4 - \log 7$

**17.** $\log_3 2x - 5\log_3 y$

**18.** $\frac{1}{3}(\log_2 x - \log_2 y)$

**19.** $\frac{1}{2}\log x + \frac{1}{3}\log y - 2\log z$   **20.** $3(4\log t^2)$

**21.** $\log_5 y - 4(\log_5 r + 2\log_5 t)$

**Expand each logarithm. Simplify if possible.**

**22.** $\log xyz$

**23.** $\log_2 \frac{x}{yz}$

**24.** $\log 6x^3 y$

**25.** $\log 7(3x - 2)^2$

**26.** $\log \sqrt{\frac{2rst}{5w}}$

**27.** $\log \frac{5x}{4y}$

**28.** $\log_5 5x^{-5}$

**29.** $\log \frac{2x^2 y}{3k^3}$

**30.** $\log_4 (3xyz)^2$

**Use the Change of Base Formula to evaluate each expression. Round your answer to the nearest thousandth.**

**31.** $\log_4 32$

**32.** $\log_3 5$

**33.** $\log_2 15$

**34.** $\log_6 17$

**35.** $\log_6 10$

**36.** $\log_5 6$

**37.** $\log_8 1$

**38.** $\log_9 11$

**39.** The concentration of hydrogen ions in a batch of homemade ketchup is $10^{-4}$. What is the pH level of the ketchup?

# 7-4 Practice (continued) Form G
## Properties of Logarithms

**Determine if each statement is *true* or *false*. Justify your answer.**

**40.** $\log 12 = \log 4 + \log 3$

**41.** $\log \frac{3}{5} = \frac{\log 3}{\log 5}$

**42.** $\log_6 12 + \log_6 3 = 2$

**43.** $\frac{1}{2} \log_4 4x = \log_4 2x$

**Use the properties of logarithms to evaluate each expression.**

**44.** $\log_2 8 - \log_2 4$

**45.** $\log_2 160 - \log_2 5$

**46.** $\log_6 27 + \log_6 8$

**47.** $\log_7 14 - \log_7 2$

**48.** $\log_4 64 + 2 \log_4 2$

**49.** $\frac{1}{4} \log_3 162 - \log_3 \sqrt[4]{2}$

**State the property or properties used to rewrite each expression.**

**50.** $\log 6 - \log 3 = \log 2$

**51.** $6 \log 2 = \log 64$

**52.** $\log 3x = \log 3 + \log x$

**53.** $\frac{1}{3} \log_2 x = \log_2 \sqrt[3]{x}$

**54.** $\frac{2}{3} \log 7 = \log \sqrt[3]{49}$

**55.** $\log_4 20 - 3 \log_4 x = \log_4 \frac{20}{x^3}$

**The formula for loudness in decibels (dB) is $L = 10 \log \dfrac{I}{I_0}$, where $I$ is the intensity of a sound in watts per square meter (W/m$^2$) and $I_0$ is $10^{-12}$ W/m$^2$, the intensity of a barely audible sound.**

**56.** A sound has an intensity of $5.92 \times 10^{25}$ W/m$^2$. What is the loudness of the sound in decibels? Use $I_0 = 10^{-12}$ W/m$^2$.

**57.** Suppose you decrease the intensity of a sound by 45%. By how many decibels would the loudness be decreased?

**58. Writing** Explain why $\log\left(\frac{9}{4}\right) \neq \dfrac{\log 9}{\log 4}$.

# 7-4 Practice

Form K

## Properties of Logarithms

| Properties of Logarithms | | |
| --- | --- | --- |
| **Product Property** | **Quotient Property** | **Power Property** |
| $\log_b mn = \log_b m + \log_b n$ | $\log_b \frac{m}{n} = \log_b m - \log_b n$ | $\log_b m^n = n \log_b m$ |

**Write each expression as a single logarithm.**

**1.** $\log_3 9 + \log_3 24$

**2.** $\log_4 16^3$

**3.** $\log_2 7 - \log_2 9$

**4.** $\log_3 8^5$

**5.** $\log_4 x - \log_4 y$

**6.** $\log 5 + \log 7$

**Expand each logarithm. Simplify if possible.**

**7.** $\log_3 27x$

**8.** $\log \frac{3}{7}$

**9.** $\log_4 y^2 z^3$

**10.** $\log_5 \frac{3^2}{x}$

**11.** $\log_3 15xy$

**12.** $\log 8xz^4$

**13. Open-Ended** Write three different logarithms. You should be able to expand each logarithm by one of the properties of logarithms.

# 7-4 Practice (continued)           Form K
## Properties of Logarithms

**Change of Base Formula**

For any positive numbers $m$, $b$, and $c$, with $b \neq 1$ and $c \neq 1$,

$$\log_b m = \frac{\log_c m}{\log_c b}$$

**Use the Change of Base Formula to evaluate each expression.**

**14.** $\log_{32} 4$

    $\dfrac{\log_2 4}{\log_2 32} =$

**15.** $\log_9 27$

**16.** $\log_4 12$

**17. Error Analysis** Your friend used the Change of Base Formula to evaluate the expression $\log_4 8$. Her answer was $\frac{2}{3}$. What error did your friend make? What is the correct answer?

**Use the following formula to solve Exercise 18.**

**Formula for Loudness of a Sound (decibels)**

$$L = 10 \log \frac{I}{I_0}$$

- $I$ is the intensity of a sound in watts per square meter ($\text{W/m}^2$).
- $I_0$ is the intensity of a sound that can barely be heard.
- $I_0 = 10^{-12}\ \text{W/m}^2$

**18.** Your classmate went to a rock concert. At the loudest point during the concert, the sound had an intensity of $2.35 \times 10^{-3}\ \text{W/m}^2$. What was the loudness of this sound in decibels?

# 7-4 Standardized Test Prep

Properties of Logarithms

## Multiple Choice

**For Exercises 1–4, choose the correct letter.**

1. Which statement correctly demonstrates the Power Property of Logarithms?

   Ⓐ $\frac{1}{2}\log_5 9 = \log_5 81$        Ⓒ $\frac{1}{2}\log_5 9 = \log_5 18$

   Ⓑ $\frac{1}{2}\log_5 9 = \log_5 \frac{9}{2}$        Ⓓ $\frac{1}{2}\log_5 9 = \log_5 3$

2. Which expression is the correct expansion of $\log_4 (3x)^2$?

   Ⓕ $\frac{1}{2}(\log_4 3 - \log_4 x)$        Ⓗ $2(\log_4 3 - \log_4 x)$

   Ⓖ $2(\log_4 3 + \log_4 x)$        Ⓘ $2\log_4 3 + \log_4 x$

3. Which expression is equivalent to $\log_7 16$?

   Ⓐ $\dfrac{\log_7 16}{\log 10}$        Ⓒ $\dfrac{\log 16}{\log 7}$

   Ⓑ $\dfrac{\log_{16} 10}{\log_7 10}$        Ⓓ $\dfrac{\log 7}{\log 16}$

4. Which statement correctly expresses $4\log_3 x + 7\log_3 y$ as a single logarithm?

   Ⓕ $\log_3 x^4 y^7$        Ⓗ $\log_3 (x^4 + y^7)$

   Ⓖ $\log_3 (4x + 7y)$        Ⓘ $\log_3 (4x - 7y)$

## Short Response

5. The pH of a substance equals $-\log[H^+]$, where $[H^+]$ is the concentration of hydrogen ions. The concentration of hydrogen ions in pure water is $10^{-7}$ and the concentration of hydrogen ions in a sodium hydroxide solution is $10^{-14}$.
   a. Without using a calculator, what is the difference of the pH levels of pure water and the sodium hydroxide solution?
   b. Explain in words or show work for how you determined the difference of the pH levels.

# 7-4 Enrichment

Properties of Logarithms

Scotsman John Napier and Joost Burgi from Switzerland are credited for being the first to introduce the concept of a logarithm. While the logarithm they described is quite different than the one we use today, both men used logarithms to simplify mathematical calculations. Arithmetic operations of addition and subtraction are relatively easy to compute, but without the modern calculator, multiplication and division of powers and roots can be time-consuming. Before calculators, logarithms were used to simplify an expression to an addition or subtraction problem. The logarithm values could be found in extensive tables and the calculations were more easily completed.

1. Consider the relation $y = \dfrac{x^{\frac{3}{4}}\sqrt{x^3}}{(3x + 2)^5}$ as an example. Without using a calculator, determine the value for $y$ when $x = 16$.

2. While the calculations in Exercise 1 are not impossible, they are certainly time-consuming and, with roots involved, are inaccurate. If you take the log base 10 of both sides, the equation becomes $\log y = \log \dfrac{x^{\frac{3}{4}}\sqrt{x^3}}{(3x + 2)^5}$. Rewrite the right side of the equation using the log properties.

To evaluate a logarithmic equation like the one above, the values were found in a table and the arithmetic calculations were completed. To get a sense of how this was done, assume you have a table of values for logarithms using base $a$. In this table you find that $\log_a 2 = 0.301$, $\log_a 3 = 0.477$, and $\log_a 5 = 0.699$.

3. Use logarithm properties to rewrite $\log_a 30$ using the three log values given. Then evaluate your expression.

4. Use logarithm properties to rewrite $\log_a 50$ and evaluate your expression.

5. Use logarithm properties to rewrite $\log_a 12.5$ and evaluate your expression.

# 7-4

## Reteaching

### Properties of Logarithms

You can write a logarithmic expression containing more than one logarithm as a single logarithm as long as the bases are equal. You can write a logarithm that contains a number raised to a power as a logarithm with the power as a coefficient. To understand the following properties, remember that logarithms are powers.

| Name | Formula | Why? |
|---|---|---|
| Product Property | $\log_b mn = \log_b m + \log_b n$ | When you multiply two powers, you add the exponents. Example: $2^6 \cdot 2^2 = 2^{(6+2)} = 2^8$ |
| Quotient Property | $\log_b \frac{m}{n} = \log_b m + \log_b n$ | When you divide two powers, you subtract the exponents. Example: $\frac{2^6}{2^2} = 2^{(6-2)} = 2^4$ |
| Power Property | $\log_b m^n = n\log_b m$ | When you raise a power to a power, you multiply the exponents. Example: $(2^6)^2 = 2^{(6 \cdot 2)} = 2^{12}$ |

### Problem

What is $2 \log_2 6 - \log_2 9 + \frac{1}{3} \log_2 27$ written as a single logarithm?

$$2 \log_2 6 - \log_2 9 + \tfrac{1}{3} \log_2 27 = \log_2 6^2 - \log_2 9 + \log_2 27^{\frac{1}{3}} \quad \text{Use the Power Property twice.}$$

$$= \log_2 36 - \log_2 9 + \log_2 3 \quad 6^2 = 36,\ 27^{\frac{1}{3}} = \sqrt[3]{27} = 3$$

$$= (\log_2 36 - \log_2 9) + \log_2 3 \quad \text{Group two of the logarithms. Use order of operations.}$$

$$= \log_2 \tfrac{36}{9} + \log_2 3 \quad \text{Quotient Property}$$

$$= \log_2 \left(\tfrac{36}{9} \cdot 3\right) \quad \text{Product Property}$$

$$= \log_2 12 \quad \text{Simplify.}$$

As a single logarithm, $2 \log_2 6 - \log_2 9 + \frac{1}{3} \log_2 27 = \log_2 12$.

# 7-4 Reteaching (continued)

Properties of Logarithms

To evaluate logarithms with any base, you can rewrite the logarithm as a quotient of two logarithms with the same base.

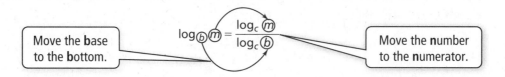

Move the base to the bottom.

$$\log_b m = \frac{\log_c m}{\log_c b}$$

Move the number to the numerator.

### Problem

What is $\log_4 8$ written as a quotient of two logarithms with base 2? Simplify your answer, if possible.

$\log_4 8 = \dfrac{\log_2 8}{\log_2 4}$    The base is 4 and the number is 8. Move the base to the bottom and the number to the numerator.

$= \dfrac{3}{2}$    Evaluate the logarithms in the numerator and the denominator.

## Exercises

**Write each logarithmic expression as a single logarithm.**

**1.** $\log_3 13 + \log_3 3$        **2.** $2 \log x + \log 5$        **3.** $\log_4 2 - \log_4 6$

**4.** $3 \log_3 3 - \log_3 3$        **5.** $\log_5 8 + \log_5 x$        **6.** $\log 2 - 2 \log x$

**7.** $\log_2 x + \log_2 y$        **8.** $3 \log_7 x - 5 \log_7 y$        **9.** $4 \log x + 3 \log x$

**10.** $\log_5 x + 3 \log_5 y$        **11.** $3 \log_2 x - \log_2 y$        **12.** $\log_2 16 - \log_2 8$

**Write each logarithm as a quotient of two common logarithms. Simplify your answer, if possible. (*Hint:* Common logarithms are logarithms with base 10.)**

**13.** $\log_4 12$        **14.** $\log_2 1000$        **15.** $\log_5 16$

**16.** $\log_{11} 205$        **17.** $\log_9 32$        **18.** $\log_{100} 51$

# 7-5 ELL Support

## Exponential and Logarithmic Equations

There are two sets of cards below that show how to solve the equation $\log_6 (x - 1) + \log_6 x = 1$. The set on the left explains the thinking. The set on the right shows the steps. Write the thinking and the steps in the correct order.

**Think Cards**

Write the equation in exponential form.

Simplify to a quadratic equation in standard form.

Apply the Product Property of logarithms.

Solve for $x$. Check for extraneous solutions.

Factor the trinomial.

**Write Cards**

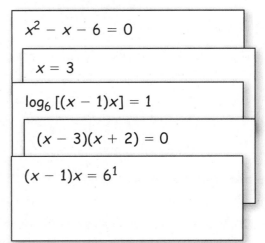

$x^2 - x - 6 = 0$

$x = 3$

$\log_6 [(x - 1)x] = 1$

$(x - 3)(x + 2) = 0$

$(x - 1)x = 6^1$

**Think**

| First, |
|---|
| Second, |
| Then, |
| Next, |
| Finally, |

**Write**

| Step 1 |
|---|
| Step 2 |
| Step 3 |
| Step 4 |
| Step 5 |

# 7-5

## Think About a Plan

Exponential and Logarithmic Equations

**Seismology** An earthquake of magnitude 7.6 occurred in 2001 in Gujarat, India. It was 251 times as strong as the greatest earthquake ever to hit Pennsylvania. What is the magnitude of the Pennsylvania earthquake? (*Hint*: Refer to the Richter scale on page 453.)

### Know

1. The magnitude of the Gujarat earthquake is ☐ .

2. The ratio of the intensity of the Gujarat earthquake to the intensity

   of Pennsylvania's greatest earthquake is ☐ .

### Need

3. To solve the problem I need to find:

   _____ .

### Plan

4. Let $I_1$ and $M_1$ be the intensity and magnitude of the Gujarat earthquake. Let $I_2$ and $M_2$ be the intensity and magnitude of Pennsylvania's greatest earthquake. What equation should you use to model this situation?

5. What does $\dfrac{I_1}{I_2}$ represent? _____

   _____

6. What can you substitute for $\dfrac{I_1}{I_2}$ in your equation?

7. Solve your equation for the magnitude of Pennsylvania's greatest earthquake.

8. The magnitude of Pennsylvania's greatest earthquake was ☐ .

# 7-5 Practice                                                    Form G

## Exponential and Logarithmic Equations

**Solve each equation.**

**1.** $8^{2x} = 32$

**2.** $7^n = 343$

**3.** $9^{2x} = 27$

**4.** $25^{2n+1} = 625$

**5.** $36^{-2x+1} = 216$

**6.** $64^x = 4096$

**Solve each equation. Round answers to the nearest hundredth.**

**7.** $5^{2x} = 20$

**8.** $8^{n+1} = 3$

**9.** $4^{n-2} = 3$

**10.** $4^{3n} = 5$

**11.** $15^{2n-3} = 245$

**12.** $4^x - 5 = 12$

**Solve by graphing. Round to the nearest hundredth.**

**13.** $2^{n+5} = 120$

**14.** $5^{n+1} = 175$

**15.** $8^x = 58$

**16.** $10^n = 3$

**17.** $10^{3y} = 5$

**18.** $10^{k-2} = 20$

**19.** $5^x = 4$

**20.** $2^{4x} = 8$

**21.** $3^{x+5} = 15$

**Use a table to solve each equation. Round to the nearest hundredth.**

**22.** $8^{2n} = 3$

**23.** $12^{2n-1} = 64$

**24.** $12^{n-2} = 8$

**25.** $10^x = 182$

**26.** $8^n = 12$

**27.** $10^{2x} = 9$

**28.** $5^{n+1} = 3$

**29.** $10^{n-2} = 0.3$

**30.** $3^{3n} = 50$

**31.** The equation $y = 281(1.01)^x$ is a model for the population of the United States $y$, in millions of people, $x$ years after the year 2000. Estimate when the United States population will reach 400 million people.

**Solve each equation. Check your answers.**

**32.** $\log x = 2$

**33.** $\log 4x = -1$

**34.** $\log 3x = 2$

**35.** $\log 4x = 2$

**36.** $4 \log x = 4$

**37.** $8 \log x = 16$

**38.** $2 \log x = 2$

**39.** $\log (2x + 5) = 3$

**40.** $\log (3x - 2) = 3$

**41.** $\log (x - 25) = 2$

**42.** $2 \log (2x + 5) = 4$

**43.** $3 \log (1 - 2x) = 6$

# 7-5

**Practice** (continued)                                     Form G

Exponential and Logarithmic Equations

**Solve each equation.**

**44.** $\log x - \log 4 = 3$     **45.** $\log x - \log 4 = -2$     **46.** $2 \log x - \log 4 = 2$

**47.** $\log 3x - \log 5 = 1$     **48.** $2 \log x - \log 3 = 1$     **49.** $\log 8 - \log 2x = -1$

**50.** $2 \log 3x - \log 9 = 1$     **51.** $2 \log x - \log 5 = -2$     **52.** $\log (x + 21) + \log x = 2$

**53.** The function $y = 1000(1.005)^x$ models the value of $1000 deposited at an interest rate of 6% per year (0.005 per month) $x$ months after the money is deposited.
    **a.** Use a graph (on your graphing calculator) to predict how many months it will be until the account is worth $1100.
    **b.** Predict how many years it will be until the account is worth $5000.

**54.** Suppose the population of a country is currently 8,100,000. Studies show this country's population is increasing 2% each year.
    **a.** What exponential function would be a good model for this country's population?
    **b.** Using the equation you found in part (a), how many years will it take for the country's population to reach 9 million? Round your answer to the nearest hundredth.

**55.** Suppose you deposit $2500 in a savings account that pays you 5% interest per year.
    **a.** How many years will it take for you to double your money?
    **b.** How many years will it take for your account to reach $8,000?

**Mental Math** Solve each equation.

**56.** $5^x = \frac{1}{25}$     **57.** $4^x = 64$     **58.** $10^x = 0.0001$

**59.** $\log_3 81 = x$     **60.** $\log_2 \frac{1}{32} = x$     **61.** $\log 1,000,000 = x$

**Use the properties of exponential and logarithmic functions to solve each system. Check your answers.**

**62.** $\begin{cases} -2^{10-x} + y = 0 \\ y = 8^{x+2} \end{cases}$     **63.** $\begin{cases} 3^{2x-y} = 1 \\ 4^{x+y} - 8 = 0 \end{cases}$     **64.** $\begin{cases} \log_2 (x - 2y) = 3 \\ \log_2 (x + y) = \log_2 8 \end{cases}$

# 7-5 Practice                                                    Form K

Exponential and Logarithmic Equations

**Solve each equation. To start, rewrite each side with a common base.**

**1.** $125^{2x} = 25$

$(5^3)^{2x} = 5^2$

$5^{6x} = 5^2$

$6x = 2$

$x =$

**2.** $2^{3x-3} = 64$

$2^{3x-3} = 2^6$

**3.** $81^{3x} = 27$

**Solve each equation. Round to the nearest ten-thousandth. Check your answers. To start, take the logarithm of each side.**

**4.** $6^{4x} = 234$

$\log 6^{4x} = \log 234$

$4x \log 6 = \log 234$

$x = \dfrac{\log 234}{4 \log 6}$

$x \approx$

**5.** $3^{5x} = 375$

$\log 3^{5x} = \log 375$

**6.** $7^{3x} - 24 = 184$

**Graphing Calculator** Solve by graphing. Round to the nearest ten-thousandth.

**7.** $3^{6x} = 2000$

Let $Y_1 = 3^{6x}$ and $Y_2 = 2000$.

$x \approx$

**8.** $8^{3x} = 154$

**9.** $12^{4x} = 4600$

**Use the following formula for Exercise 10.**

$$T(m) = a(1 + r)^m$$

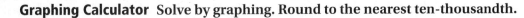

- $m$ = the number of minutes it takes for $\frac{3}{4}$ of the crowd to leave the stadium
- $T(m)$ = the number of people in the stadium after $m$ minutes
- $a$ = the number of people currently in the stadium
- $r$ = the percent change in the number of people in the stadium

**10.** There are currently 100,000 people in a stadium watching a soccer game. When the game ends, about 3% of the crowd will leave the stadium each minute. At this rate, how many minutes will it take for $\frac{3}{4}$ of the crowd to leave the stadium?

## 7-5 **Practice** (continued)

Exponential and Logarithmic Equations

**Convert from Logarithmic Form to Exponential Form to solve each equation.**

| Exponential and Logarithmic Form | |
| --- | --- |
| Logarithmic Form $\log_b x = y$ | Exponential Form $b^y = x$ |

**11.** $\log(2x + 4) = 3$

$2x + 4 = 10^3$

$2x = 996$

$x =$

**12.** $\log 4z - 3 = 2$

$\log 4z = 5$

**13.** $\log(2x - 8) = 2$

**Use the properties of logarithms to solve each equation.**

| Product Property | Quotient Property | Power Property |
| --- | --- | --- |
| $\log_b mn = \log_b m + \log_b n$ | $\log_b \frac{m}{n} = \log_b m - \log_b n$ | $\log_b m^n = n \log_b m$ |

**14.** $2 \log x + \log 4 = 3$

$\log x^2 + \log 4 = 3$

$\log 4x^2 = 3$

$4x^2 = 10^3$

$x^2 = 250$

$x \approx$

**15.** $\log y - \log 4 = 2$

$\log \frac{y}{4} = 2$

**16.** $\log 10 + \log 2x = 3$

**17. Error Analysis** Your friend used the following steps to solve the equation $\log x + \log 6 = 4$. What error did he make? What is the correct answer?

$\log x + \log 6 = 4$

$\log \frac{x}{6} = 4$

$\frac{x}{6} = 10^4$

$x = 6000$

# 7-5 Standardized Test Prep

Exponential and Logarithmic Equations

## Multiple Choice

**For Exercises 1–5, choose the correct letter.**

1. If $9^x = 243$, what is the value of $x$?

   (A) 2       (B) 5       (C) 2.5       (D) 10

2. If $2^{3x+2} = 64$, what is the value of $x$?

   (F) $\dfrac{8}{3}$       (G) $\dfrac{4}{3}$       (H) 2       (I) $\dfrac{3}{4}$

3. If $\log(3x + 25) = 2$, what is the value of $x$?

   (A) 25       (B) 75       (C) $41\frac{2}{3}$       (D) 100

4. Which best approximates the solution of $16^{2x} = 124$?

   (F) 0.869       (G) 1.150       (H) 1.739       (I) 3.477

5. Which equation represents the solution of $2^{3x+1} = 7$?

   (A) $x = 3\left(\dfrac{\log 7}{\log 2} - 1\right)$       (C) $x = \dfrac{1}{3}\left(\dfrac{\log 2}{\log 7} - 1\right)$

   (B) $x = \dfrac{\log 7}{3\log 2} - 1$       (D) $x = \dfrac{1}{3}\left(\dfrac{\log 7}{\log 2} - 1\right)$

## Short Response

6. In 2007, the population of Tallahassee, Florida was 168,979. Some researchers believe that the population of Tallahassee will increase at a rate of 1% each year for the 10 years following this.
   a. If the researchers are correct, how many years will it take for the population of Tallahassee to reach 180,000?
   b. Explain in words or show your work for how you determined the number of years found in part (a).

# 7-5  Enrichment

## Exponential and Logarithmic Equations

When solving logarithm equations, you primarily use the Product Property, Quotient Property, and Power Property to simplify the equation. Here is an interesting, lesser-known property of logarithms to explore.

**1.** Determine the value of each pair of expressions.

$\log_2 4, \log_4 2$

$\log_3 81, \log_{81} 3$

$\log_{10} 1000, \log_{1000} 10$

**2.** How are the values of each pair of expressions related?

**3.** This reciprocal property states that $\log_a b = \dfrac{1}{\log_b a}$. To prove this property, assume $r = \log_a b$ and $s = \log_b a$. Rewrite each of these equations in exponential form.

**4.** Next, use one equation to substitute an equivalent expression in for $a$. What is your new equation?

**5.** Use the laws of exponents to simplify.

**6.** Because the bases are the same, what equation can you write for the exponents?

**7.** What must be true about $s$ and $r$ if the product equals 1?

**8.** Use this new property to solve the equation $\log_5 x + \dfrac{1}{\log_x 5} = 4$.

# 7-5    Reteaching

### Exponential and Logarithmic Equations·

Use logarithms to solve exponential equations.

### Problem

What is the solution of $7 - 5^{2x-1} = 4$?

| | |
|---|---|
| $7 - 5^{2x-1} = 4$ | |
| $-5^{2x-1} = -3$ | First isolate the term that has the variable in the exponent. Begin by subtracting 7 from each side. |
| $5^{2x-1} = 3$ | Multiply each side by $-1$. |
| $\log_5 5^{2x-1} = \log_5 3$ | Because the variable is in the exponent, use logarithms. Take $\log_5$ of each side because 5 is the base of the exponent. |
| $(2x - 1)\log_5 5 = \log_5 3$ | Use the Power Property of Logarithms. |
| $2x - 1 = \log_5 3$ | Simplify. (Recall that $\log_b b = 1$.) |
| $2x - 1 = \dfrac{\log 3}{\log 5}$ | Apply the Change of Base Formula. |
| $2x = \dfrac{\log 3}{\log 5} + 1$ | Add 1 to each side. |
| $x = \dfrac{1}{2}\left(\dfrac{\log 3}{\log 5} + 1\right)$ | Divide each side by 2. |
| $x \approx 0.84$ | Use a calculator to find a decimal approximation. |

## Exercises

Solve each equation. Round the answer to the nearest hundredth.

**1.** $2^x = 5$          **2.** $10^{2x} = 8$          **3.** $5^{x+1} = 25$

**4.** $2^{x+3} = 9$          **5.** $3^{2x-3} = 7$          **6.** $4^x - 5 = 3$

**7.** $5 + 2^{x+6} = 9$          **8.** $4^{3x} + 2 = 3$          **9.** $1 - 3^{2x} = -5$

**10.** $2^{3x} - 2 = 13$          **11.** $5^{2x+7} - 1 = 8$          **12.** $7 - 2^{x+7} = 5$

## 7-5 Reteaching (continued)

Exponential and Logarithmic Equations

Use exponents to solve logarithmic equations.

**Problem**

What is the solution of $8 - \log(4x - 3) = 4$?

| | |
|---|---|
| $8 - \log(4x - 3) = 4$ | |
| $-\log(4x - 3) = -4$ | First isolate the term that has the variable in the logarithm. Begin by subtracting 8 from each side. |
| $\log(4x - 3) = 4$ | Multiply each side by –1. |
| $4x - 3 = 10^4$ | Write in exponential form. |
| $4x - 3 = 10{,}000$ | Simplify. |
| $4x = 10{,}003$ | Add 3 to each side. |
| $x = \dfrac{10{,}003}{4}$ | Solve for $x$. |
| $x = 2500.75$ | Divide. |

## Exercises

**Solve each equation. Round the answer to the nearest thousandth.**

**13.** $\log x = 2$

**14.** $\log 3x = 3$

**15.** $\log 2x + 2 = 6$

**16.** $5 + \log(2x + 1) = 6$

**17.** $\log 5x + 62 = 62$

**18.** $6 - \log\frac{1}{2}x = 3$

**19.** $\log(4x - 3) + 6 = 4$

**20.** $\frac{2}{3}\log 5x = 2$

**21.** $2\log 250x - 6 = 4$

**22.** $5 - 2\log x = \frac{1}{2}$

# 7-6 ELL Support

## Natural Logarithms

**Problem**

What is the solution of the equation $3e^{4x} + 5 = 26$? Explain your work and check your solution.

| | |
|---|---|
| $3e^{4x} + 5 = 26$ | Write the original equation. |
| $3e^{4x} = 21$ | Subtract 5 from each side. |
| $e^{4x} = 7$ | Divide each side by 3. |
| $4x = \ln 7$ | Rewrite in logarithmic form. |
| $x = 0.25 \ln 7$ | Divide each side by 4. |
| $x \approx 0.486$ | Use a calculator. |

**Check**

| | |
|---|---|
| $3e^{4x} + 5 = 26$ | Write the original equation. |
| $3e^{4(0.486)} + 5 = 26$ | Substitute 0.486 for $x$. |
| $25.96 \approx 26$ | Use a calculator. |

## Exercise

What is the solution of the equation $5e^{2x} - 2 = 12$? Explain your work and check your solution.

| | |
|---|---|
| $5e^{2x} - 2 = 12$ | _____ |
| $5e^{2x} = 14$ | _____ |
| $e^{2x} = 2.8$ | _____ |
| $2x = \ln 2.8$ | _____ |
| $x = 0.5 \ln 2.8$ | _____ |
| $x \approx 0.515$ | _____ |

**Check**

| | |
|---|---|
| $5e^{2x} - 2 = 12$ | _____ |
| $5e^{2(0.515)} - 2 = 12$ | _____ |
| $12.005 \approx 12$ | _____ |

## 7-6 Think About a Plan

Natural Logarithms

**Archaeology** A fossil bone contains 25% of its original carbon-14. What is the approximate age of the bone?

### Understanding the Problem

1. What is the amount of carbon-14 remaining in the fossil bone?

   _____

2. If $a$ is the amount of carbon-14 originally in an object and $t$ is the object's age in years, what equation gives the amount of carbon-14 in the object?

3. What is the problem asking you to determine?

   _____

### Planning the Solution

4. What number should you substitute for $y$ in the equation above?

5. Write an equation you can use to determine the approximate age of the bone.

### Getting an Answer

6. How can logarithms help you solve your equation?

   _____

   _____.

7. Solve your equation to find the approximate age of the bone.

# 7-6 Practice                                    Form G
Natural Logarithms

**Write each expression as a single natural logarithm.**

**1.** $\ln 16 - \ln 8$

**2.** $3 \ln 3 + \ln 9$

**3.** $a \ln 4 - \ln b$

**4.** $\ln z - 3 \ln x$

**5.** $\frac{1}{2} \ln 9 + \ln 3x$

**6.** $4 \ln x + 3 \ln y$

**7.** $\frac{1}{3} \ln 8 + \ln x$

**8.** $3 \ln a - b \ln 2$

**9.** $2 \ln 4 - \ln 8$

**Solve each equation. Check your answers. Round your answer to the nearest hundredth.**

**10.** $4 \ln x = -2$

**11.** $2 \ln (3x - 4) = 7$

**12.** $5 \ln (4x - 6) = -6$

**13.** $-7 + \ln 2x = 4$

**14.** $3 - 4 \ln (8x + 1) = 12$

**15.** $\ln x + \ln 3x = 14$

**16.** $2 \ln x + \ln x^2 = 3$

**17.** $\ln x + \ln 4 = 2$

**18.** $\ln x - \ln 5 = -1$

**19.** $\ln e^x = 3$

**20.** $3 \ln e^{2x} = 12$

**21.** $\ln e^{x+5} = 17$

**22.** $\ln 3x + \ln 2x = 3$

**23.** $5 \ln (3x - 2) = 15$

**24.** $7 \ln (2x + 5) = 8$

**25.** $\ln (3x + 4) = 5$

**26.** $\ln \frac{2x}{41} = 2$

**27.** $\ln (2x - 1)^2 = 4$

**Use natural logarithms to solve each equation. Round your answer to the nearest hundredth.**

**28.** $e^x = 15$

**29.** $4e^x = 10$

**30.** $e^{x+2} = 50$

**31.** $4e^{3x-1} = 5$

**32.** $e^{x-4} = 2$

**33.** $5e^{6x+3} = 0.1$

**34.** $e^x = 1$

**35.** $e^{\frac{x}{5}} = 32$

**36.** $3e^{3x-5} = 49$

**37.** $7e^{5x+8} = 0.23$

**38.** $6 - e^{12x} = 5.2$

**39.** $e^{\frac{x}{2}} = 25$

**40.** $e^{2x} = 25$

**41.** $e^{\ln 5x} = 20$

**42.** $e^{\ln x} = 21$

**43.** $e^{x+6} + 5 = 1$

# 7-6

**Practice** (continued)

Natural Logarithms

Form G

The formula $P = 50e^{-\frac{t}{25}}$ gives the power output $P$, in watts, needed to run a certain satellite for $t$ days. Find how long a satellite with the given power output will operate.

**44.** 10 W                    **45.** 12 W                    **46.** 14 W

The formula for the maximum velocity $v$ of a rocket is $v = -0.0098t + c \ln R$, where $c$ is the exhaust velocity in km/s, $t$ is the firing time, and $R$ is the mass ratio of the rocket. A rocket must reach 7.7 km/s to attain a stable orbit 300 km above Earth.

**47.** What is the maximum velocity of a rocket with a mass ratio of 18, an exhaust velocity of 2.2 km/s, and a firing time of 25 s?

**48.** Can the rocket in Exercise 47 achieve a stable orbit? Explain your answer.

**49.** What mass ratio would be needed to achieve a stable orbit for a rocket with an exhaust velocity of 2.5 km/s and a firing time of 29 s?

**50.** A rocket with an exhaust velocity of 2.4 km/s and a 28 second firing time can reach a maximum velocity of 7.8 km/s. What is the mass ratio of the rocket?

By measuring the amount of carbon-14 in an object, a paleontologist can determine its approximate age. The amount of carbon-14 in an object is given by $y = ae^{-0.00012t}$, where $a$ is the amount of carbon-14 originally in the object, and $t$ is the age of the object in years.

**51.** A fossil of a bone contains 32% of its original carbon-14. What is the approximate age of the bone?

**52.** A fossil of a bone contains 83% of its original carbon-14. What is the approximate age of the bone?

**Simplify each expression.**

**53.** $\ln e^4$            **54.** $5 \ln e^5$            **55.** $\dfrac{\ln e^2}{2}$            **56.** $\ln e^{100}$

# 7-6 Practice

Form K

Natural Logarithms

**Write each expression as a single logarithm. The first expression is simplified for you.**

**1.** $\ln 3 + \ln 4$

$\ln(3 \cdot 4)$

**2.** $3\ln x - \ln 5$

$\ln x^3 - \ln 5$

**3.** $(\ln 3x + \ln 4) - \ln 8$

**Solve each equation. Round your answers to the nearest tenth. The first equation is solved for you.**

**4.** $\ln(3x + 1) = 4$

$3x + 1 = e^4$

$3x = e^4 - 1$

$3x \approx 53.6$

$x =$

**5.** $\ln(y - 2) = 3$

$y - 2 = e^3$

**6.** $3\ln 2x = 3$

**Use the following formula to complete Exercises 7 and 8.**

| Maximum Velocity of a Rocket |
| --- |
| $v = -0.0098t + c\ln R$ |
| • $v$ = maximum velocity<br>• $t$ = rocket's firing time<br>• $c$ = velocity of exhaust<br>• $R$ = mass ratio of the rocket |

**7.** A rocket has a mass ratio of 24. The rocket's exhaust has a velocity of 2.4 km/s. The rocket's firing time is 32 seconds. Approximately what is the rocket's maximum velocity? Round to the nearest tenth.

**8.** The rocket in Exercise 7 was changed to prepare it for a new mission. The new mass ratio is 26, and the new exhaust velocity is 2.3 km/s. Will these changes increase or decrease the rocket's maximum velocity? What is the difference between the maximum velocities?

# 7-6

## Practice (continued)

### Natural Logarithms

**Solve each equation. Round your answers to the nearest thousandth.**

**9.** $2e^{4x} - 4 = 10$

$2e^{4x} = 14$

$e^{4x} = 7$

$4x = \ln 7$

$x = 0.25 \ln 7$

$x \approx$

**10.** $e^{\frac{x}{2}} + 6 = 12$

$e^{\frac{x}{2}} = 6$

$\frac{x}{2} = \ln 6$

**11.** $e^{x-2} = 28$

**12.** $e^{\frac{x}{4}} - 3 = 21$

**13.** $e^{x+2} + 4 = 17$

**14.** $3e^{\frac{x}{2}} - 5 = 19$

**15. Writing** Explain the steps you would follow to solve the equation $4e^{3x} + 6 = 30$. What is the answer?

**Use the following formula to complete Exercise 16.**

| Bacteria Culture Decline |
| --- |
| $$H = \frac{1}{r}(\ln P - \ln A)$$ |

- $H$ = number or hours
- $r$ = rate of decline
- $P$ = initial bacteria population
- $A$ = reduced bacteria population

**16.** A scientist tests an antibiotic that causes a rate of decline of 0.18. About how long will it take this antibiotic to shrink a population of 4000 bacteria to 300? Round your answer to the nearest hundredth.

# 7-6 Standardized Test Prep

### Natural Logarithms

## Multiple Choice

**For Exercises 1–4, choose the correct letter. Do not use a calculator.**

1. What is $3 \ln 5 - \ln 2$ written as a single natural logarithm?

   Ⓐ $\ln 7.5$      Ⓑ $\ln 27$      Ⓒ $\ln \left(\frac{5}{2}\right)^3$      Ⓓ $\ln 62.5$

2. What is the solution of $e^{x+1} = 13$?

   Ⓕ $x = \ln 13 + 1$    Ⓖ $x = \ln 13 - 1$    Ⓗ $x = \ln 13$    Ⓘ $x = \ln 12$

3. What is the solution of $\ln(x - 2)^2 = 6$?

   Ⓐ $2 + e^3$      Ⓑ $2 - e^3$      Ⓒ $2 \pm e^3$      Ⓓ $2 \pm e^6$

4. What is the solution of $e^{\frac{x}{2}+1} + 3 = 8$?

   Ⓕ $x = 2\ln 5 - 1$    Ⓖ $x = 2\ln 5 - 2$    Ⓗ $x = 2\ln 4$    Ⓘ $x = \frac{1}{2}(\ln 5 - 1)$

## Short Response

5. The maximum velocity $v$ of a rocket is $v = -0.0098t + c\ln R$. The rocket
   fires for $t$ seconds and the velocity of the exhaust is $c$ km/s. The ratio of the
   mass of the rocket filled with fuel to the mass of the rocket without fuel is $R$.
   A spacecraft can attain a stable orbit 300 km above Earth if it reaches a velocity
   of 7.7 km/s.
   a. What is the velocity of a spacecraft whose booster rocket has a mass ratio of
      16, an exhaust velocity of 3.2 km/s, and a firing time of 40 s?
   b. Can this rocket attain a stable orbit 300 km above Earth? Explain in words or
      show work for how you determined your answer.

# 7-6  Enrichment

### Natural Logarithms

## Calculating Natural Logarithms

You can compute natural logarithms with

$$\ln x = \frac{(x-1)^1}{1} - \frac{(x-1)^2}{2} + \frac{(x-1)^3}{3} - \frac{(x-1)^4}{4} + \frac{(x-1)^5}{5} - \cdots$$

where the pattern continues forever. Notice that there are actually three patterns involved as the terms progress.

**1.** What is the pattern of the signs?

**2.** What is the pattern of the exponents?

**3.** What is the pattern of the denominators?

**4.** For $x = 1$, what is the sum of the series?

**5.** Use a calculator to fill in the blanks in the following chart to four decimal places. Then compare your results with the value of $\ln x$ obtained directly.

| | $x = 1.1$ | $x = 1.5$ |
|---|---|---|
| $\dfrac{(x-1)^1}{1}$ | | |
| $-\dfrac{(x-1)^2}{2}$ | | |
| Result | | |
| $+\dfrac{(x-1)^3}{3}$ | | |
| Result | | |
| $-\dfrac{(x-1)^4}{4}$ | | |
| Result | | |
| $+\dfrac{(x-1)^5}{5}$ | | |
| Result | | |
| $\ln x$ | | |

# 7-6 Reteaching
## Natural Logarithms

The **natural logarithmic function** is a logarithm with base $e$, an irrational number.

You can write the natural logarithmic function as $y = \log_e x$, but you usually write it as $y = \ln x$.

$y = e^x$ and $y = \ln x$ are inverses, so if $y = e^x$, then $x = \ln y$.

To solve a natural logarithm equation:
- If the term containing the variable is an exponential expression, rewrite the equation in logarithmic form.
- If term containing the variable is a logarithmic expression, rewrite the equation in exponential form.

### Problem

What is the solution of $4e^{2x} - 2 = 3$?

**Step 1** Isolate the term containing the variable on one side of the equation.

$$4e^{2x} - 2 = 3$$

$$4e^{2x} = 5 \qquad \text{Add 2 to each side of the equation.}$$

$$e^{2x} = \frac{5}{4} \qquad \text{Divide each side of the equation by 4.}$$

**Step 2** Take the natural logarithm of each side of the equation.

$$\ln\left(e^{2x}\right) = \ln\left(\tfrac{5}{4}\right)$$

$$2x = \ln\left(\tfrac{5}{4}\right) \qquad \text{Definition of natural logarithm}$$

**Step 3** Solve for the variable.

$$x = \frac{\ln\left(\tfrac{5}{4}\right)}{2} \qquad \text{Divide each side of the equation by 2.}$$

$$x \approx 0.112 \qquad \text{Use a calculator.}$$

**Step 4** Check the solution.

$$4e^{2(0.112)} - 2 \stackrel{?}{=} 3$$

$$4e^{0.224} - 2 \stackrel{?}{=} 3$$

$$3.004 \approx 3$$

The solution is $x \approx 0.112$.

Prentice Hall Algebra 2 • Teaching Resources
59

# 7-6 Reteaching (continued)

Natural Logarithms

### Problem

What is the solution of $\ln(t - 2)^2 + 1 = 6$? Round your answer to the nearest thousandth.

**Step 1** Isolate the term containing the variable on one side of the equation.

$$\ln(t - 2)^2 + 1 = 6$$

$$\ln(t - 2)^2 = 5 \qquad \text{Subtract 1 from each side of the equation.}$$

**Step 2** Raise each side of the equation to the base $e$.

$$e^{\ln(t-2)^2} = e^5$$

$$(t - 2)^2 = e^5 \qquad \text{Definition of natural logarithm}$$

**Step 3** Solve for the variable.

$$t - 2 = \pm e^{\frac{5}{2}} \qquad \text{Take the square root of each side of the equation.}$$

$$t = 2 \pm e^{\frac{5}{2}} \qquad \text{Add 2 to each side of the equation.}$$

$$t \approx 14.182 \text{ or } -10.182 \qquad \text{Use a calculator.}$$

**Step 4** Check the solution.

$$\ln(14.182 - 2)^2 \overset{?}{=} 5 \qquad \ln(-10.182 - 2)^2 \overset{?}{=} 5$$

$$4.9999 \approx 5 \qquad 4.9999 \approx 5$$

The solutions are $t \approx 14.182$ and $-10.182$.

## Exercises

**Use natural logarithms to solve each equation. Round your answer to the nearest thousandth. Check your answers.**

**1.** $2e^x = 4$        **2.** $e^{4x} = 25$        **3.** $e^x = 72$

**4.** $e^{3x} = 124$        **5.** $12e^{3x-2} = 8$        **6.** $\frac{1}{2}e^{6x} = 5$

**Solve each equation. Round your answer to the nearest thousandth. Check your answers.**

**7.** $\ln(x - 3) = 2$        **8.** $\ln 2t = 4$        **9.** $1 + \ln x^2 = 2$

**10.** $\ln(2x - 5) = 3$        **11.** $\frac{1}{3}\ln 2t = 1$        **12.** $\ln(t - 4)^2 + 2 = 5$

# Chapter 7 Quiz 1

Form G

Lessons 7-1 through 7-3

## Do you know HOW?

**1.** For the function $y = 5^{(x-2)}$, identify the transformation of the parent function $y = 5^x$.

Write each equation in logarithmic form.

**2.** $64 = 8^2$       **3.** $8 = 2^3$       **4.** $125 = 5^3$       **5.** $729 = 3^6$

Graph each function. Then find the domain, range, and *y*-intercept.

**6.** $y = 5^x - 2$       **7.** $y = 3(2)^x$       **8.** $y = \left(\frac{1}{2}\right)^x$

Evaluate each logarithm.

**9.** $\log_3 243$       **10.** $\log_5 625$       **11.** $\log_9 729$       **12.** $\log_4 256$

## Do you UNDERSTAND?

**13. Error Analysis** A classmate says that $y = \left(\frac{3}{2}\right)^x$ represents exponential decay. What is the student's mistake?

**14. Writing** Explain how you would graph an exponential function.

**15. Reasoning** Find the value of $\log_8 64$ without using a calculator. Justify your answer.

# Chapter 7 Quiz 2

Form G

Lessons 7-4 through 7-6

## Do you know HOW?

**Solve each equation. Round your answer to the nearest hundredth.**

**1.** $\ln 3x = 8$

**2.** $\frac{1}{2} \ln 5x = 4$

**3.** $\ln (x - 4) = 2$

**Write each expression as a single logarithm.**

**4.** $\log_5 3 + \log_5 6$

**5.** $\log_2 32 - \log_2 8$

**6.** $\frac{1}{2} \log_4 25 + \log_4 2$

**Solve each equation.**

**7.** $4^x = 16$

**8.** $9^{y-3} = 81$

**9.** $\log \frac{1}{3} x = 2$

**Expand each logarithm.**

**10.** $\log_4 \frac{m}{n}$

**11.** $\log_5 \left( x \cdot \sqrt[3]{y} \right)$

**12.** $\log_3 \frac{x^4}{y^2}$

## Do you UNDERSTAND?

**13. Vocabulary** What is an exponential equation?

**14. Open-Ended** Write $\log 27$ as a sum or difference of two logarithms. Simplify if possible.

**15. Vocabulary** What is the base of the natural logarithmic function $y = \ln x$?

**16. Reasoning** Explain how you could find the value of $\log_{16} 64$ without using a calculator?

# Chapter 7 Chapter Test

*Form G*

## Do you know HOW?

Solve each equation.

**1.** $8 - 3^x = -1$

**2.** $\log_3 81 = x$

**3.** $\log x - \log 3 = 2$

**4.** You put $2000 into an account earning 4% interest compounded continuously. Find the amount in the account at the end of 8 years.

Describe how the graph of each function is related to the graph of its parent function.

**5.** $y = -2^x + 1$

**6.** $y = 3^{x-4}$

**7.** $y = 5^{x+1} - 2$

Evaluate each logarithm.

**8.** $\log_5 125$

**9.** $\log_{\frac{1}{2}} \frac{1}{4}$

**10.** $\log_3 729$

**11.** $\log_9 \frac{1}{3}$

**12.** $\log_{\frac{1}{4}} 16$

**13.** $\log_8 \frac{1}{256}$

Write each equation in logarithmic form.

**14.** $7^3 = 343$

**15.** $\left(\frac{2}{3}\right)^{-3} = \frac{27}{8}$

**16.** $2^{-4} = 0.0625$

Write each logarithmic expression as a single logarithm.

**17.** $\log 2 + 3 \log 1$

**18.** $\log a - \log ab$

**19.** $\frac{1}{3}(\log_4 x + \log_4 z)$

# Chapter 7 Chapter Test (continued)                    Form G

**Use the Change of Base Formula to rewrite each expression using common logarithms.**

**20.** $\log_4 12$        **21.** $\log_2 5$        **22.** $\log_8 14$

**23.** A parent increases a child's allowance by 15% each year. If the allowance is $3 now, when will it reach $15?

**24.** A scientist notes that the number of bacteria in a colony is 50. Two hours later, she notes that the number of bacteria has increased to 80. If this rate of growth continues, how much more time will it take for the number of bacteria to reach 100?

**Graph each function.**

**25.** $y = -3^x + 1$        **26.** $y = \log_5 x$        **27.** $y = \log(x + 1)$

## Do you UNDERSTAND?

**28. Writing** Describe the effect of different values of $a$ on the function $y = ab^x$.

**29. Vocabulary** State which property or properties need to be used to write each expression as a single logarithm.
   **a.** $\log_6 16 - \log_6 4$        **b.** $2\log_2 3 + \log_2 4$

**30. Reasoning** Identify each function as *linear*, *quadratic*, or *exponential*. Explain your reasoning.
   **a.** $y = 4(2)^x$
   **b.** $y = 6(x)^2 + 1$

**31. Writing** Explain the difference between exponential growth and exponential decay.

# Chapter 7 Quiz 1

Form K

Lessons 7–1 through 7–3

## Do you know HOW?

Without graphing, determine whether the function represents exponential growth or decay.

**1.** $y = 2(1.05)^x$

**2.** $y = 4\left(\frac{3}{5}\right)^x$

**3.** $y = 3(0.45)^x$

Identify the parent of each function. Then graph each function as a transformation of its parent function.

**4.** $y = 0.25 \cdot 4^x$

**5.** $y = 2^{x-1} - 2$

Evaluate each logarithm.

**6.** $\log_5 125$

**7.** $\log_{27} 9$

**8.** $\log_8 128$

## Do you UNDERSTAND?

**9.** In March, a town was hit by an earthquake with a magnitude of 7.3 on the Richter scale. The same town was hit by an earthquake with a magnitude of 6.4 in June. How many times more intense was the earthquake in March? Use the formula $\log \frac{I_1}{I_2} = M_1 - M_2$ to solve the problem.

**10.** Fran has $2400 invested in a savings account. The account pays 4% annual interest. How much money will be in the account after 8 years? Use the formula $A(t) = a(1 + r)^t$.

# Chapter 7 Quiz 2

Form K

Lessons 7–4 through 7–5

## Do you know HOW?

Write each expression as a single logarithm.

**1.** $\log_3 24 + \log_3 2$

**2.** $\log_2 12 - \log_2 3$

**3.** $3 \log x + 5 \log y$

Expand each logarithm.

**4.** $\log_7 \frac{23}{4}$

**5.** $\log_2 32x^3$

**6.** $\log_6 \frac{x^4}{38}$

Use the Change of Base Formula to evaluate each expression.

**7.** $\log_{125} 25$

**8.** $\log_7 25$

**9.** $\log_5 40$

Solve each equation.

**10.** $27^{4x} = 9$

**11.** $\log(6x - 2) = 3$

**12.** $\log 4 + \log x = 2$

## Do you UNDERSTAND?

**13.** The population of fish in a lake is decreasing. There are currently 24,000 fish in the lake. The population is decreasing by 6% each year. In how many years will there be $\frac{1}{4}$ of the current number of fish in the lake? Use the formula $T(n) = a(1 + r)^n$ to solve the problem.

**14.** A scientist is calculating the pH levels of vinegar and dish detergent. He uses the formula $\text{pH} = -\log[\text{H}^+]$. $[\text{H}^+{}_v]$ for vinegar is $6.3 \times 10^{-3}$. $[\text{H}^+{}_d]$ for dish detergent is $10^{-12}$. What is the difference of the pH levels for vinegar and dish detergent?

# Chapter 7 Test

## Do you know HOW?

Determine whether each function is an example of exponential growth or decay. Then find the *y*-intercept.

**1.** $y = 4(0.85)^x$

**2.** $y = 18(1.03)^x$

**3.** $y = 9(2.25)^x$

Evaluate each logarithm.

**4.** $\log_9 81$

**5.** $\log_{64} 4$

**6.** $\log_4 8$

## Do you UNDERSTAND?

**7. Writing** Explain how you can tell whether the function $y = a \log_b x$ is a vertical stretch or a compression of its parent function.

**8.** Robert invested $800 in a bank account. The account has an annual interest rate of 5.5%. How much money will be in the account after 12 years? Use the formula $A(t) = P \cdot e^{rt}$ to solve the problem.

**9.** In 1985, Mexico was hit by an earthquake with a magnitude of 8.1 on the Richter scale. Eight years later, India was hit by an earthquake with a magnitude of 6.0. How many times more intense was the earthquake in Mexico than the earthquake in India? Use the formula $\log \frac{I_1}{I_2} = M_1 - M_2$.

# Chapter 7 Test (continued)

Form K

## Do you know HOW?

Use the Change of Base Formula to evaluate each expression.

**10.** $\log_{32} 8$        **11.** $\log_7 42$        **12.** $\log_{26} 5$

Use the properties of logarithms to solve the following logarithmic equations.

**13.** $2 \log 5 + \log x = 2$     **14.** $\log (x - 21) + \log x = 2$     **15.** $\log 4x - \log 5 = 3$

## Do you UNDERSTAND?

**16. Error Analysis** A math test contained the equation $25^{2x} = 35$. A student used the equation $(5^2)^{2x} = 5^7$ to find his answer of $x = 1.75$. What error did the student make? What is the correct answer?

**17.** There was a fireworks display in Downsville last night. The first burst during the display made a sound with an intensity of $3.14 \times 10^{-4} \, \text{W/m}^2$. During the last burst, the sound reached an intensity of $4.25 \times 10^{-3} \, \text{W/m}^2$. How many decibels louder was the last burst than the first burst? Use the formula $L = 10 \log \frac{I}{I_0}$, where $I_0 = 10^{-12}$.

**18.** The population of a bee colony is growing at a rate of 2.3% each year. There are currently 3400 bees in the colony. At this rate, in how many years will there be 10,200 bees in the colony? Use the formula $T(y) = a(1 + r)^y$ to solve the problem.

# Chapter 7 Performance Tasks

**Give complete answers.**

## Task 1

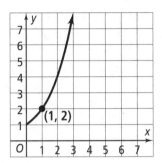

a. Write an exponential function that could model the information in this graph.

b. Describe a business, scientific (not mathematical), or economic situation for what this graph might represent. Include how the different mathematical aspects of the graph affect the situation.

c. How will the graph and situation change when you change the base of this exponential function?

d. Describe the conditions under which the function represents a growth or decay situation.

## Task 2

a. Write a detailed description of how logarithms can be used to solve exponential equations and how exponents can be used to solve logarithmic equations.

b. Give and solve an example of each type of equation.

c. Explain why using logarithms and exponents to solve equations that contain the other is an important concept in mathematics.

## Chapter 7 Performance Tasks (continued)

### Task 3

a. State the three Properties of Logarithms.

b. Give an example for using each property.

c. Describe a real-life situation in which you would apply one or more of the properties. Show how you would use them.

### Task 4

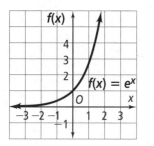

a. What is the inverse of $f(x)$?

b. Graph the inverse function from part (a).

c. Rewrite the inverse function from part (a) in exponential form.

d. Evaluate the inverse function from part (a) for $x = 1$ and $x = e$.

# Chapter 7 Cumulative Review

## Multiple Choice

**For Exercises 1–10, choose the correct letter.**

1. Which of the following systems is *dependent*?

   Ⓐ $\begin{cases} y = 2x - 1 \\ y = -2x + 2 \end{cases}$     Ⓑ $\begin{cases} y = 2x - 1 \\ y = 2x + 3 \end{cases}$     Ⓒ $\begin{cases} y = 2x - 1 \\ 2y = 4x - 2 \end{cases}$     Ⓓ $\begin{cases} y = 2x - 1 \\ y = -\frac{1}{2}x + 1 \end{cases}$

2. The electric current $I$ in amperes (A) of a circuit is given by the formula $\log_2 I = -t$. Find the current when $t$ is 3 s.

   Ⓕ $-0.903$ A     Ⓖ $0.125$ A     Ⓗ $0.405$ A     Ⓘ $0.794$ A

3. Which of the following functions represent exponential growth?

   Ⓐ $y = 50(0.50)^x$     Ⓑ $y = \frac{1}{2}(1.1)^x$     Ⓒ $y = 2\left(\frac{3}{8}\right)^x$     Ⓓ $y = 15(0.98)^x$

4. What is the next number in the pattern $1, -2, 4, -8, 16, \ldots$ ?

   Ⓕ $-32$     Ⓖ $24$     Ⓗ $32$     Ⓘ $-24$

5. Use the Change of Base Formula to rewrite $\log_7 16$ using common logarithms.

   Ⓐ $\dfrac{\log_7 16}{\log 10}$     Ⓑ $\dfrac{\log 7}{\log 16}$     Ⓒ $\dfrac{\log_{16} 10}{\log_{10} 7}$     Ⓓ $\dfrac{\log 16}{\log 7}$

6. Which of the following is the vertex of the function $y = -|2x| + 1$?

   Ⓕ $(0, 2)$     Ⓖ $(2, 0)$     Ⓗ $(0, 1)$     Ⓘ $(1, 0)$

7. What is the simplified form of the expression $\sqrt[4]{x^{20} y^8}$?

   Ⓐ $x^5 y^2$     Ⓑ $|x^5| y^2$     Ⓒ $x^5 |y^2|$     Ⓓ $|x^5 y^2|$

8. Which of the following represents the polynomial $6x + 3x^2 - 2$ in standard form?

   Ⓕ $-2 + 6x + 3x^2$     Ⓗ $-2 + 3x^2 + 6x$

   Ⓖ $3x^2 + 6x - 2$     Ⓘ $6x + 3x^2 - 2$

# Chapter 7 Cumulative Review (continued)

9. Which of the following is $2 \ln 10 - \ln 5$ written as a single natural logarithm?

   Ⓐ $\ln 2$        Ⓑ $\ln 4$        Ⓒ $\ln 15$        Ⓓ $\ln 20$

10. Which of the following is the correct expansion of $\log_6 \dfrac{x^2 y}{z^4}$?

   Ⓕ $\log_6 2x + \log_6 y - \log_6 4z$        Ⓗ $2 \log_6 x + \log_6 y - 4 \log_6 z$

   Ⓖ $2 \log_6 x \cdot \log_6 y \div 4 \log_6 z$        Ⓘ $2 \log_6 xy + 4 \log_6 z$

## Short Response

11. For the years 2000–2005, the median price of a single-family home in the United States can be approximated by the exponential function $A = 227{,}200(1.087)^t$, where $t$ is the number of years after the year 2000.

    a. What is the growth rate of housing prices for this period?

    b. What was the median price of a single-family home in the year 2005?

12. Order the expressions below from least to greatest. Show your work.

    $5^2$        $\log_5 2$        $2^5$        $\log_2 5$        $\log 5$

13. Solve the inequality $|2x + 2| > 4$. Graph the solution.

## Extended Response

14. You and your friend are saving for college. You have $50 and are adding $10 each week to your savings. Your friend has $20 and he is adding $20 each week to his savings.

    a. What system of equations would be a good model for this situation? Let $x$ be number of weeks and $y$ be the number of dollars saved.

    b. Graph your system of equations.

    c. Use your graph to determine when you and your friend will have the same amount of money saved. Explain your answer.

# Chapter 7 Project Teacher Notes: Crime Time

## About the Project

The Chapter Project gives students the opportunity to explore how mathematics is used in forensic science. Students investigate the validity of the alibi of a suspect of a crime by using Newton's Law of Cooling. They verify formulas by using natural logarithms to solve equations. Students use these equations to calculate information that will help them prove or disprove the suspect's alibi. They present their conclusions in an investigative report.

## Introducing the Project

- Ask students if they are familiar with the field of forensic science.
- Discuss information that can help indict a crime suspect.
- Have students review direct variation.

## Activity 1: Investigating

Students consider information that can help prove or disprove a crime suspect's alibi.

## Activity 2: Writing

Students use direct variation to write an equation for Newton's Law of Cooling.

## Activity 3: Solving

Students use natural logarithms to solve equations.

## Activity 4: Calculating

Students calculate how long ago a car's engine was running at its normal operating temperature.

## Finishing the Project

You may wish to plan a project day on which students share their completed projects. Encourage students to explain their processes as well as their results. Ask students to review their project work and update their folders.

- Have students review any information needed in order to be able to prove or disprove the alibi. Have them summarize how they solved the formulas used in the project.
- Ask groups to share their insights that resulted from completing the project, such as any shortcuts they found for solving formulas or for researching information.

# Chapter 7 Project: Crime Time

## Beginning the Chapter Project

Forensic science is the application of science to law. A forensic scientist investigates evidence that can help place a suspect at the scene of a crime. Each piece of forensic evidence may help build a successful case against a suspect in a court of law.

In this project, you will examine how mathematics can be used by forensic scientists to help indict people suspected of criminal actions.

### List of Materials

- Calculator

## Activities

### Activity 1: Investigating

A major crime occurred at approximately 10:15 P.M. Shortly thereafter, a certain make and model car, along with its license plate number, were recorded by a witness who reportedly had seen the car speeding in the vicinity of the crime scene. Police and forensic scientists immediately went to the home of the person to whom the car was registered, where they found the car parked in the driveway. The investigation team noted that it had taken them 30 minutes to travel to the suspect's home from the crime scene. They also noted that the engine of the car was still warm when they arrived at 11:00 P.M. When confronted, the suspect claimed to have been at a friend's house earlier that night and had returned home at about 10:00 P.M. The suspect's friend confirmed the alibi, and reported calling the suspect at home at about 10:00 P.M., and having a conversation with the suspect until about 10:20 P.M. What information can investigators use to help prove or disprove the suspect's alibi? Explain.

### Activity 2: Writing

As police questioned the suspect, the team of forensic scientists began to take temperature measurements of the vehicle's engine coolant, knowing that this information could help determine how long it had been since the engine had been running. In order to determine this time, forensic scientists use Newton's Law of Cooling. This law states that the change in temperature of an object over time $t$, denoted $T'$, varies directly with the difference between the temperature of the object $T$ and the temperature of the surrounding environment, or ambient temperature, $A$. Letting $-k$ represent the constant of variation for a positive value of $k$, write an equation to represent Newton's Law of Cooling.

## Chapter 7 Project: Crime Time (continued)

### Activity 3: Solving

Using calculus and the equation you wrote in Activity 2, the team determined that the temperature of an object after time $t$ in minutes is given by the formula $T(t) = A + (T_0 - A)e^{-kt}$, where $T_0$ represents the temperature at time $t = 0$. Verify that the constant of variation can be found by using the formula $k = -\frac{1}{t_1}\ln\left(\frac{T_1 - A}{T_0 - A}\right)$, where $T_1$ represents the temperature at some later time $t_1$. Then, verify that $t_n$, the time the engine stopped running at a normal operating temperature, is given by $t_n = -\frac{1}{k}\ln\left(\frac{T_n - A}{T_0 - A}\right)$, where $T_n$ represents the normal operating temperature of the engine.

### Activity 4: Calculating

When the team began investigating at 11:00 P.M., the initial temperature of the engine's coolant was 150°F. By 11:10 P.M. the temperature had dropped to 130°F. The ambient temperature was 70°F. The normal running temperature of the car's engine, based on its make and model, is about 200°F. Let $t = 0$ represent 11:00 P.M.

- Using this information and the equations from Activity 3, first determine the value of $k$, then determine the value of $t_n$. What does this information tell you? Explain.

- If the suspect's car had been turned off at 10:00 P.M., what would the temperature reading have been at 11:00 P.M.?

### Finishing the Project

The activities should help you complete your project. Prepare a presentation in the form of an investigative report, providing evidence that will help clear or indict the suspect. Present your report to your classmates. Then discuss the data that helped you to reach your conclusion(s).

### Reflect and Revise

Ask a small group of classmates to review your report. Is your information presented clearly? Have you sufficiently explained why the evidence helps to prove or disprove the suspect's alibi? Make any necessary changes and improvements before presenting your project to the class.

### Extending the Project

Discuss other evidence that an investigator could use to place a suspect at a crime scene. Research how mathematics can be applied to other crime scene evidence. If possible, interview a forensic scientist.

# Chapter 7 Project Manager: Crime Time

## Getting Started

Read the project. As you work on the project, you will need a calculator and materials on which you can record your calculations. Keep all of your work for the project in a folder.

### Checklist

☐ Activity 1: analyzing information

☐ Activity 2: using Newton's Law of Cooling

☐ Activity 3: verifying formulas

☐ Activity 4: using formulas

### Suggestions

☐ Consider all the given times and the time of the alleged phone call.

☐ Review direct variation (Lesson 2-2).

☐ Use $(t_1, T_1)$ in the temperature equation to solve for $k$. Then, use $(t_n, T_n)$ in the temperature equation to solve for $t_n$.

☐ Identify $t_1$, $T_0$, $T_1$, and $A$. Then, identify $T_n$.

## Scoring Rubric

**4** Calculations and equations are correct. Explanations are thorough, clear, and well thought out. The investigative report is well organized and presents the information in a logical manner.

**3** Calculations and equations are mostly correct with some minor errors. Explanations are mostly accurate and complete. The investigative report is not well organized.

**2** Calculations and equations contain both minor and major errors. Explanations and the investigative report are incomplete or inaccurate.

**1** Major concepts are misunderstood. Project satisfies few of the requirements and shows poor organization and effort.

**0** Major elements of the project are incomplete or missing.

**Your Evaluation of Project** Evaluate your work, based on the *Scoring Rubric*.

## Teacher's Evaluation of the Project

**Prentice Hall Algebra 2** • Teaching Resources
76

**page 1**

### 7-1 ELL Support
Exploring Exponential Models

Choose the word or phrase from the list that best completes each sentence.

| | | |
|---|---|---|
| exponential function | exponential growth | exponential decay |
| asymptote | growth factor | decay factor |

1. In the function $y = 12(2.3)^x$, the value 2.3 is the **growth factor**.

2. An **asymptote** is a line that a graph approaches as $x$ or $y$ increases in absolute value.

3. For **exponential decay**, as the value of $x$ increases, the value of $y$ decreases.

4. A function in the general form $y = ab^x$ is called an **exponential function**.

5. For **exponential growth**, as the value of $x$ increases, the value of $y$ increases.

6. In the function $y = 4(0.3)^x$, the value 0.3 is the **decay factor**.

Identify whether each function represents exponential growth or exponential decay.

7. $y = 0.75(4)^x$    exponential growth

8. $y = 0.63(0.5)^x$    exponential decay

9. $y = 9(0.83)^x$    exponential decay

10. $y = 12(7)^x$    exponential growth

Identify the $y$-intercept for each function.

11. $y = 4.5(7)^x$    **4.5**

12. $y = 5(3.2)^x$    **5**

**page 2**

### 7-1 Think About a Plan
Exploring Exponential Models

**Population** The population of a certain animal species decreases at a rate of 3.5% per year. You have counted 80 of the animals in the habitat you are studying.
 a. Write a function that models the change in the animal population.
 b. **Graphing Calculator** Graph the function. Estimate the number of years until the population first drops below 15 animals.

1. Is an exponential model reasonable for this situation? Explain.

   Yes; the population decreases at a fixed, constant rate of 3.5% per year.

   An exponential model is reasonable

2. Write the function that models exponential growth or decay. $A(t) = \boxed{a(1 + r)^t}$

3. The initial population is $\boxed{80\ \text{animals}}$.

4. Is the rate of change positive or negative? Explain.

   The population is decreasing, so the rate of change is negative

5. The rate of change is $\boxed{-0.035}$.

6. Write a function that models the change in the animal population. $P(t) = \boxed{80(0.965)^t}$

7. Graph your function on a graphing calculator. Sketch your graph.

8. How can you find the $x$-value that produces a given $y$-value?

   Answers may vary. Sample: Use the TRACE function

9. Use your graph to estimate the number of years until the population first drops below 15 animals.  **47 years**

**page 3**

### 7-1 Practice                                        Form G
Exploring Exponential Models

Graph each function.

1. $y = (0.3)^x$

2. $y = 3^x$

3. $y = 2\left(\frac{1}{5}\right)^x$

4. $y = \frac{1}{2}(3)^x$

5. $s(t) = 2.5^t$

6. $f(x) = \frac{1}{2}(5)^x$

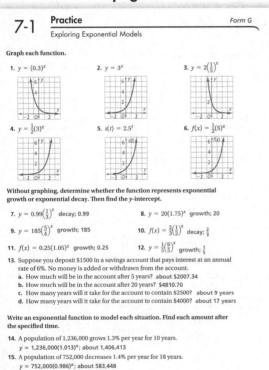

Without graphing, determine whether the function represents exponential growth or exponential decay. Then find the $y$-intercept.

7. $y = 0.99\left(\frac{1}{3}\right)^x$    decay; 0.99

8. $y = 20(1.75)^x$    growth; 20

9. $y = 185\left(\frac{5}{4}\right)^x$    growth; 185

10. $f(x) = \frac{2}{3}\left(\frac{1}{2}\right)^x$    decay; $\frac{2}{3}$

11. $f(x) = 0.25(1.05)^x$    growth; 0.25

12. $y = \frac{1}{5}\left(\frac{6}{5}\right)^x$    growth; $\frac{1}{5}$

13. Suppose you deposit $1500 in a savings account that pays interest at an annual rate of 6%. No money is added or withdrawn from the account.
 a. How much will be in the account after 5 years?  about $2007.34
 b. How much will be in the account after 20 years?  $4810.70
 c. How many years will it take for the account to contain $2500?  about 9 years
 d. How many years will it take for the account to contain $4000?  about 17 years

Write an exponential function to model each situation. Find each amount after the specified time.

14. A population of 1,236,000 grows 1.3% per year for 10 years.
 $y = 1,236,000(1.013)^x$; about 1,406,413

15. A population of 752,000 decreases 1.4% per year for 18 years.
 $y = 752,000(0.986)^x$; about 583,448

16. A new car that sells for $18,000 depreciates 25% each year for 4 years.
 $y = 18,000(0.75)^x$; $5695.31

**page 4**

### 7-1 Practice (continued)                            Form G
Exploring Exponential Models

For each annual rate of change, find the corresponding growth or decay factor.

17. +45%  1.45     18. −10%  0.9     19. −40%  0.6     20. +200%  3

21. +28%  1.28     22. +100%  2      23. −5%  0.95     24. +3%  1.03

25. In 2009, there were 1570 bears in a wildlife refuge. In 2010, the population had increased to approximately 1884 bears. If this trend continues and the bear population is increasing exponentially, how many bears will there be in 2010?
 8100 bears

26. The value of a piece of equipment has a decay factor of 0.80 per year. After 5 years, the equipment is worth $98,304. What was the original value of the equipment?  $300,000

27. Your friend drops a rubber ball from 4 ft. You notice that its rebound is 32.5 in. on the first bounce and 22 in. on the second bounce.
 a. What exponential function would be a good model for the height of the ball?  $y = 48(0.677)^x$
 b. How high will the ball bounce on the fourth bounce?  about 10.08 in.

28. An investment of $75,000 increases at a rate of 12.5% per year. What is the value of the investment after 30 years?  $2,568,247.87

29. A new truck that sells for $29,000 depreciates 12% each year. What is the value of the truck after 7 years?  $11,851.59

30. The price of a new home is $350,000. The value of the home appreciates 2% each year. How much will the home be worth in 10 years?  $426,648.05

31. The population of an endangered bird is decreasing at a rate of 0.75% per year. There are currently about 200,000 of these birds.
 a. What exponential function would be a good model for the population of these endangered birds?  $y = 200,000(0.9925)^x$
 b. How many birds will there be in 100 years?  almost 94,207 birds

## page 5

**7-1 Practice** Form K

Exploring Exponential Models

Complete the table of values for each function. Then graph the function.

**1.** $y = 3^x$

| x | $3^x$ | y |
|---|---|---|
| −2 | $3^{-2}$ | 0.11 |
| −1 | $3^{-1}$ | 0.33 |
| 0 | $3^0$ | 1 |
| 1 | $3^1$ | 3 |
| 2 | $3^2$ | 9 |

**2.** $y = 0.5(2)^x$

| x | $0.5(2)^x$ | y |
|---|---|---|
| −1 | $0.5(2)^{-1}$ | 0.25 |
| 0 | $0.5(2)^0$ | 0.5 |
| 1 | $0.5(2)^1$ | 1 |
| 2 | $0.5(2)^2$ | 2 |
| 3 | $0.5(2)^3$ | 4 |
| 4 | $0.5(2)^4$ | 8 |

**3.** $y = 3(2)^x$

| x | $3(2)^x$ | y |
|---|---|---|
| −2 | $3(2)^{-2}$ | 0.75 |
| −1 | $3(2)^{-1}$ | 1.5 |
| 0 | $3(2)^0$ | 3 |
| 1 | $3(2)^1$ | 6 |
| 2 | $3(2)^2$ | 12 |

**4.** $y = 2(0.5)^x$

| x | $2(0.5)^x$ | y |
|---|---|---|
| −2 | $2(0.5)^{-2}$ | 8 |
| −1 | $2(0.5)^{-1}$ | 4 |
| 0 | $2(0.5)^0$ | 2 |
| 1 | $2(0.5)^1$ | 1 |
| 2 | $2(0.5)^2$ | 0.5 |

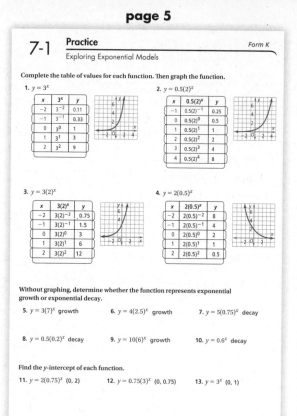

Without graphing, determine whether the function represents exponential growth or exponential decay.

**5.** $y = 3(7)^x$  growth

**6.** $y = 4(2.5)^x$  growth

**7.** $y = 5(0.75)^x$  decay

**8.** $y = 0.5(0.2)^x$  decay

**9.** $y = 10(6)^x$  growth

**10.** $y = 0.6^x$  decay

Find the y-intercept of each function.

**11.** $y = 2(0.75)^x$  (0, 2)

**12.** $y = 0.75(3)^x$  (0, 0.75)

**13.** $y = 3^x$  (0, 1)

## page 6

**7-1 Practice** (continued) Form K

Exploring Exponential Models

For each annual rate of change, find the corresponding growth or decay factor.

**14.** 35%  1.35

**15.** −20%  0.8

**16.** 62%  1.62

**17.** Identify the meaning of the variables in the exponential growth or decay function.

$$A(t) = a(1 + r)^t$$

a. $a =$ the initial amount

b. $r =$ the rate of growth or decay

c. $t =$ the number of time periods

**18.** The population of Bainsville is 2000. The population is supposed to grow by 10% each year for the next 5 years. How many people will live in Bainsville in 5 years?  3221

**19. Writing** Describe a situation that could be modeled by the function $A(t) = 200(1.05)^x$. Answers may vary. Sample: Someone deposits $200 into a bank account that earns 5% interest each year.

**20.** A music store sold 200 guitars in 2007. The store sold 180 guitars in 2008. The number of guitars that the store sells is decreasing exponentially. If this trend continues, how many guitars will the store sell in 2012?

$r = \dfrac{y_2 - y_1}{y_1}$

$r = \dfrac{180 - 200}{200}$

$r = -0.1$

$A(t) = a(1 + r)^t$

$A(5) = 200(1 - 0.1)^5 \approx 118$ guitars

## page 7

**7-1 Standardized Test Prep**

Exploring Exponential Models

**Multiple Choice**

For Exercises 1 and 2, choose the correct letter.

**1.** Which of the following functions represents exponential decay and has a y-intercept of 2? D

Ⓐ $y = 2\left(\frac{4}{3}\right)^x$

Ⓒ $y = \frac{1}{4}(2)^x$

Ⓑ $y = \frac{1}{2}(0.95)^x$

Ⓓ $y = 2\left(\frac{2}{5}\right)^x$

**2.** Suppose you deposit $3000 in a savings account that pays interest at an annual rate of 4%. If no other money is added or withdrawn from the account, how much will be in the account after 10 years? H

Ⓕ $3122.18

Ⓗ $4440.73

Ⓖ $4994.50

Ⓘ $86,776.40

**Extended Response**

**3.** In 2009 there was an endangered population of 270 cranes in a western state. Due to wildlife efforts, the population is increasing at a rate of 5% per year.

a. What exponential function would be a good model for this population of cranes? Explain in words or show work for how you determined the exponential function.

b. If this trend continues, how many cranes will there be in this population in 2020? Show your work.

[4] a. The general form of an exponential function is $y = a(b)^x$. x represents time in years, y represents the population of cranes, and a is the initial value of 270 cranes. Because the crane population is increasing by 5%, $b = 1 + r = 1 + 0.05 = 1.05$. The exponential function that models the crane population is $y = 270(1.05)^x$ OR equivalent explanation.

b. $y = 270(1.05)^{11} \approx 461.79$; almost 462 cranes

[3] appropriate methods and correct function, but with one computational error in evaluating the function

[2] incorrect function or multiple computational errors in evaluating the function

[1] correct function and population, without work shown

[0] incorrect answers and no work shown OR no answers given

## page 8

**7-1 Enrichment**

Exploring Exponential Models

**Determining Relationships Between Variables**

On the basis of data, scientists sometimes hypothesize that a quantity z depends on two quantities x and y such that

$$z = Cx^r y^s$$

where C is a constant and r and s are integers. By doing experiments in which the values of x and y are varied, they determine the values of integers r and s.

For instance, suppose the momentum M of a moving object seems to be related to the mass m and velocity v by the equation $M = Cm^r v^s$. Later, scientists find that doubling the mass and keeping the velocity constant doubles the momentum, so

$$2M = C(2m)^r v^s.$$

Using substitution and simplifying:  $2(Cm^r v^s) = C2^r m^r v^s$

Dividing each side by $Cm^r v^s$:  $2 = 2^r$

$1 = r$

**1.** Suppose that doubling the velocity while holding the mass constant also doubles the momentum. Express this relationship in an equation.  $2M = Cm^r(2v)^s$

**2.** Solve your equation for s.  $s = 1$

**3.** Use the values of r and s to write an expression for momentum in terms of mass m, velocity v, and the constant C.  $M = Cmv$

**Use a similar method to solve the following problems.**

**4.** The price P of a diamond is related to both the weight W of the diamond and its brilliance B. If both the weight and brilliance are simultaneously doubled, the price of the diamond increases by a factor of 32. If the weight is doubled and, at the same time, the brilliance is halved, the price increases by a factor of 2. Write a formula for P in terms of W, B, and the constant C.  $P = CW^3B^2$

**5.** The price of wheat depends upon the weight and the water content. A particular wheat trader pays according to this pattern: the price P increases by a factor of 2 when the weight is doubled and the water content is constant. If the weight is doubled and the water content is halved, the price is constant. Write a formula for P in terms of weight w, water content h, and the constant C.  $P = Cwh$

## page 9

### 7-1 Reteaching
Exploring Exponential Models

- The general form of an exponential function is $y = ab^x$, where $a$ is the initial amount and $b$ is the growth or decay factor.
- To find $b$, use the formula $b = 1 + r$, where $r$ is the constant rate of growth or decay. If $r$ is a rate of growth, it will be positive. If $r$ is a rate of decay, it will be negative. Therefore, if $b$ is greater than 1, the function models growth. If $b$ is between zero and 1, the function models decay. When you see words like *increase* or *appreciation*, think growth. When you see words like *decrease* or *depreciation*, think decay.
- For an exponential function, the $y$-intercept is always equal to the value of $a$.

**Problem**

Carl's weight at 12 yr is 82 lb. Assume that his weight increases at a rate of 16% each year. Write an exponential function to model the increase. What is his weight after 5 years?

**Step 1** Find $a$ and $b$.

$a = 82$     $a$ is the original amount.

$b = 1 + 0.16$     $b$ is the growth or decay factor. Since this problem models growth, $r$ will be positive. Make sure to rewrite the rate, $r$, as a decimal.

$= 1.16$

**Step 2** Write the exponential function.

$y = ab^x$     Use the formula.

$y = 82(1.16)^x$     Substitute.

**Step 3** Calculate.

$y = 82(1.16)^5$     Substitute 5 for $x$.

$y \approx 172.228$     Use a calculator.

Carl will weigh about 172 lb in 5 years.

**Exercises**

Determine whether the function represents exponential growth or exponential decay. Then find the $y$-intercept.

1. $y = 8000(1.15)^x$   growth; 8000
2. $y = 20(0.75)^x$   decay; 20
3. $y = 15\left(\frac{1}{2}\right)^x$   decay; 15
4. $f(x) = 6\left(\frac{5}{2}\right)^x$   growth; 6

## page 10

### 7-1 Reteaching (continued)
Exploring Exponential Models

You can use the general form of an exponential function to solve word problems involving growth or decay.

**Problem**

A motorcycle purchased for $9000 today will be worth 6% less each year. How much will the motorcycle be worth at the end of 5 years?

**Step 1** Find $a$ and $b$.

$a = 9000$     $a$ is the original amount.

$b = 1 + (-0.06)$     $b$ is the growth or decay factor. Since this problem models decay, $r$ will be negative. Make sure to rewrite the rate, $r$, as a decimal.

$= 0.94$

**Step 2** Write the exponential function.

$y = ab^x$     Use the formula.

$y = 9000(0.94)^x$     Substitute.

**Step 3** Calculate.

$y = 9000(0.94)^5$     Substitute 5 for $x$.

$y \approx 6605.13$     Use a calculator.

The motorcycle will be worth about $6605.13 after 5 years.

**Exercises**

Write an exponential function to model each situation. Find each amount after the specified time.

5. A tree 3 ft tall grows 8% each year. How tall will the tree be at the end of 14 yr? Round the answer to the nearest hundredth.   $y = 3(1.08)^x$; 8.81 ft

6. The price of a new home is $126,000. The value of the home appreciates 2% each year. How much will the home be worth in 10 yr?   $y = 126,000(1.02)^x$; $153,593.29

7. A butterfly population is decreasing at a rate of 0.82% per year. There are currently about 100,000 butterflies in the population. How many butterflies will there be in the population in 250 years?   $y = 100,000(0.9918)^{250}$; 12,765 butterflies

8. A car depreciates 10% each year. If you bought this car today for $5000, how much will it be worth in 7 years?   $y = 5000(0.90)^7$; $2391.48

## page 11

### 7-2 ELL Support
Properties of Exponential Functions

**Concept List**

| | |
|---|---|
| compression | continuously compounded interest |
| horizontal translation 3 units to the right | natural base exponential function |
| parent function | reflection in $x$-axis |
| stretch | vertical translation 3 units upward |

Choose the concept from the list above that best represents the item in each box.

| | |
|---|---|
| 1. $y = 3 \cdot 5^x$ <br> stretch | 2. $y = 0.67^x$ <br> parent function |
| 3. $y = 7^x + 3$ <br> vertical translation 3 units upward | 4. $A(t) = P \cdot e^{rt}$ <br> continuously compounded interest |
| 5. $y = -7^x$ <br> reflection in $x$-axis | 6. $y = 0.56(7)^x$ <br> compression |
| 7. $y = e^5$ <br> natural base exponential function | 8. $y = 11^{(x-3)}$ <br> horizontal translation 3 units to the right |

## page 12

### 7-2 Think About a Plan
Properties of Exponential Functions

**Investment** How long would it take to double your principal in an account that pays 6.5% annual interest compounded continuously?

**Know**

1. The equation for continuously compounded interest is $\boxed{A(t) = P \cdot e^{rt}}$.

2. The principal is $\boxed{P}$.

3. The interest rate is $\boxed{0.065}$.

**Need**

4. To solve the problem I need to:

    find the time $t$ when the amount in the account is twice the original principal .

**Plan**

5. If the principal is $P$, then twice the principal is $\boxed{2P}$.

6. What equation can you use to find the time it takes to double your principal?   $2P = P \cdot e^{rt}$

7. Solve your equation for $t$.

$$2P = P \cdot e^{rt}$$
$$2 = e^{rt}$$
$$\ln 2 = \ln e^{rt}$$
$$\ln 2 = rt$$
$$t = \frac{\ln 2}{r} = \frac{\ln 2}{0.065} \approx 10.7 \text{ years}$$

8. Is your solution reasonable? Explain.

    Yes; it seems reasonable that it would take almost 11 years to double

    the principal

**page 13**

**page 14**

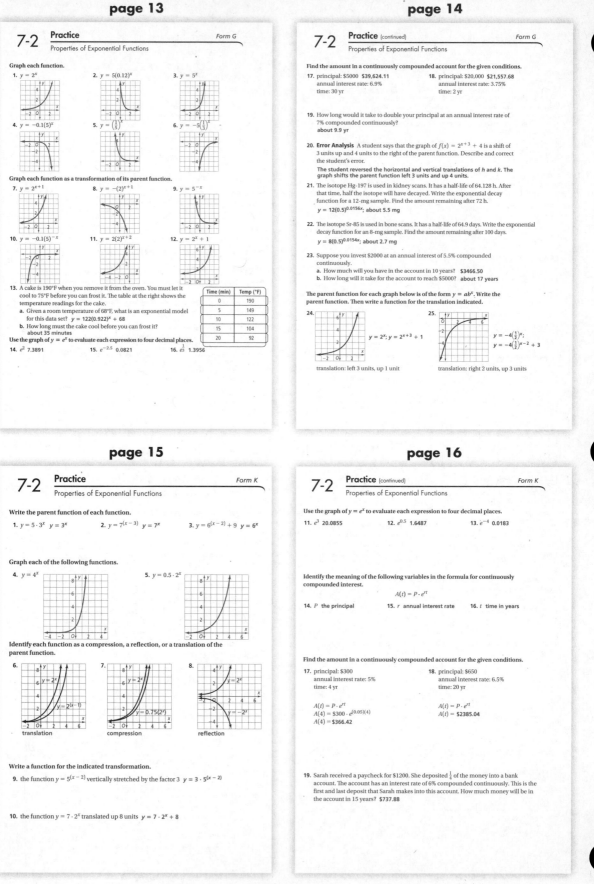

### page 13

**7-2 Practice** Form G
Properties of Exponential Functions

**Graph each function.**

1. $y = 2^x$
2. $y = 5(0.12)^x$
3. $y = 5^x$

4. $y = -0.1(5)^x$
5. $y = \left(\frac{1}{5}\right)^x$
6. $y = -5\left(\frac{1}{3}\right)^x$

**Graph each function as a transformation of its parent function.**

7. $y = 2^{x+1}$
8. $y = -(2)^{x+1}$
9. $y = 5^{-x}$

10. $y = -0.1(5)^{-x}$
11. $y = 2(2)^{x+2}$
12. $y = 2^x + 1$

13. A cake is 190°F when you remove it from the oven. You must let it cool to 75°F before you can frost it. The table at the right shows the temperature readings for the cake.
   a. Given a room temperature of 68°F, what is an exponential model for this data set? $y = 122(0.922)^x + 68$
   b. How long must the cake cool before you can frost it?
      about 35 minutes

| Time (min) | Temp (°F) |
|---|---|
| 0 | 190 |
| 5 | 149 |
| 10 | 122 |
| 15 | 104 |
| 20 | 92 |

**Use the graph of $y = e^x$ to evaluate each expression to four decimal places.**

14. $e^2$  7.3891
15. $e^{-2.5}$  0.0821
16. $e^{\frac{1}{3}}$  1.3956

### page 14

**7-2 Practice** (continued) Form G
Properties of Exponential Functions

**Find the amount in a continuously compounded account for the given conditions.**

17. principal: $5000  **$39,624.11**
    annual interest rate: 6.9%
    time: 30 yr

18. principal: $20,000  **$21,557.68**
    annual interest rate: 3.75%
    time: 2 yr

19. How long would it take to double your principal at an annual interest rate of 7% compounded continuously?
    about 9.9 yr

20. **Error Analysis** A student says that the graph of $f(x) = 2^{x+3} + 4$ is a shift of 3 units up and 4 units to the right of the parent function. Describe and correct the student's error.
    **The student reversed the horizontal and vertical translations of h and k. The graph shifts the parent function left 3 units and up 4 units.**

21. The isotope Hg-197 is used in kidney scans. It has a half-life of 64.128 h. After that time, half the isotope will have decayed. Write the exponential decay function for a 12-mg sample. Find the amount remaining after 72 h.
    $y = 12(0.5)^{0.0156x}$; about 5.5 mg

22. The isotope Sr-85 is used in bone scans. It has a half-life of 64.9 days. Write the exponential decay function for an 8-mg sample. Find the amount remaining after 100 days.
    $y = 8(0.5)^{0.0154x}$; about 2.7 mg

23. Suppose you invest $2000 at an annual interest of 5.5% compounded continuously.
    a. How much will you have in the account in 10 years?  $3466.50
    b. How long will it take for the account to reach $5000?  about 17 years

The parent function for each graph below is of the form $y = ab^x$. Write the parent function. Then write a function for the translation indicated.

24. $y = 2^x$; $y = 2^{x+3} + 1$
    translation: left 3 units, up 1 unit

25. $y = -4\left(\frac{1}{2}\right)^x$;
    $y = -4\left(\frac{1}{2}\right)^{x-2} + 3$
    translation: right 2 units, up 3 units

**page 15**

**page 16**

### page 15

**7-2 Practice** Form K
Properties of Exponential Functions

**Write the parent function of each function.**

1. $y = 5 \cdot 3^x$   $y = 3^x$
2. $y = 7^{(x-3)}$   $y = 7^x$
3. $y = 6^{(x-2)} + 9$   $y = 6^x$

**Graph each of the following functions.**

4. $y = 4^x$
5. $y = 0.5 \cdot 2^x$

**Identify each function as a compression, a reflection, or a translation of the parent function.**

6. $y = 2^x$, $y = 2^{(x-1)}$
   translation
7. $y = 2^x$, $y = 0.75(2^x)$
   compression
8. $y = 2^x$, $y = -2^x$
   reflection

**Write a function for the indicated transformation.**

9. the function $y = 5^{(x-2)}$ vertically stretched by the factor 3  $y = 3 \cdot 5^{(x-2)}$

10. the function $y = 7 \cdot 2^x$ translated up 8 units  $y = 7 \cdot 2^x + 8$

### page 16

**7-2 Practice** (continued) Form K
Properties of Exponential Functions

**Use the graph of $y = e^x$ to evaluate each expression to four decimal places.**

11. $e^3$  20.0855
12. $e^{0.5}$  1.6487
13. $e^{-4}$  0.0183

**Identify the meaning of the following variables in the formula for continuously compounded interest.**

$$A(t) = P \cdot e^{rt}$$

14. $P$  the principal
15. $r$  annual interest rate
16. $t$  time in years

**Find the amount in a continuously compounded account for the given conditions.**

17. principal: $300
    annual interest rate: 5%
    time: 4 yr

    $A(t) = P \cdot e^{rt}$
    $A(4) = $300 \cdot e^{(0.05)(4)}$
    $A(4) = $366.42$

18. principal: $650
    annual interest rate: 6.5%
    time: 20 yr

    $A(t) = P \cdot e^{rt}$
    $A(t) = $2385.04$

19. Sarah received a paycheck for $1200. She deposited $\frac{1}{4}$ of the money into a bank account. The account has an interest rate of 6% compounded continuously. This is the first and last deposit that Sarah makes into this account. How much money will be in the account in 15 years?  $737.88

## page 17

### 7-2 Standardized Test Prep
Properties of Exponential Functions

**Gridded Response**

Solve each exercise and enter your answer in the grid provided.

1. Suppose you deposit $6000 in a savings account that pays interest at an annual rate of 4% compounded continuously. How many years will it take for the balance in your savings account to reach $8000? Round your answer up to the nearest number of years.

2. Suppose you make $1500 at your summer job and you decide to invest this money in a savings account that pays interest at an annual rate of 5.5% compounded continuously. How many dollars will be in the account after 5 years? Express the answer to the nearest whole dollar.

3. The half-life of a radioactive substance is the time it takes for half of the material to decay. Phosphorus-32 is used to study a plant's use of fertilizer. It has a half-life of 14.3 days. How many milligrams of phosphorus-32 remain after 92 days from a 100-mg sample? Express the answer to the nearest whole milligram.

4. A scientist notes the bacteria count in a petrie dish is 40. Three hours later, she notes the count has increased to 75. Using an exponential model, how many hours will it take for the bacteria count to grow from 75 to 120? Express the answer to the nearest tenth of an hour.

**Answers**

1. 8   2. 1975   3. 1   4. 2.2

## page 18

### 7-2 Enrichment
Properties of Exponential Functions

**A Closer Look at Compounding**

The formula for finding the amount of money accumulated in an account is

$A = P(1 + \frac{r}{n})^{nt}$.

The variable **P** represents the **principal**, or amount initially invested.
The variable **r** represents the interest **rate** as a decimal.
The variable **n** represents the number of times per year the interest is **compounded**.
The variable **t** represents the **time**, or number of years for which the money is invested.

1. $750 is invested at 11% compounded quarterly. How much is in the account after 10 yr? **$2219.9**

2. Write the new formula for P = $1, r = 1.0, and t = 1 yr. $A = 1(1 + \frac{1}{n})^n$

3. Remember that n is the number of times the interest is compounded. What happens as n grows? In other words, what is the effect of compounding more often? Fill in the following table. Round answers to eight decimal places.

| $n$ | $\left(1 + \frac{1}{n}\right)^n$ |
|---|---|
| 1 | 2.00000000 |
| 10 | 2.59374246 |
| 100 | 2.70481383 |
| 1,000 | 2.71692393 |
| 10,000 | 2.71814593 |
| 100,000 | 2.71826824 |
| 1,000,000 | 2.71828047 |
| 10,000,000 | 2.71828169 |
| 100,000,000 | 2.71828181 |
| 1,000,000,000 | 2.71828183 |

4. The table suggests that as n increases, the value of $\left(1 + \frac{1}{n}\right)^n$ gets closer to [        ]. If the value of n is increased further, the decimal approximation in the table will get very close to the value of a number known as e. This number is used in many growth and decay applications. **2.71828183**

5. As n grows, you get closer to compounding continuously. This is why the formula used for compounding continuously is $A = Pe^{rt}$. Rework Exercise 1 assuming that compounding is continuous. **$2253.12**

## page 19

### 7-2 Reteaching
Properties of Exponential Functions

There are four types of transformations that can change the graph of an exponential function.

**Stretches**
The factor a in $y = ab^x$ can stretch the graph of an exponential function when $|a| > 1$

**Compressions**
The factor a in $y = ab^x$ can compress the graph of an exponential function when $0 < |a| < 1$

**Reflections**
The factor a in $y = ab^x$ can reflect the graph of an exponential function in the x-axis when $a < 0$

**Translations**
The graph of an exponential function translates horizontally by h; vertically by k.
$y = ab^{(x-h)} + k$

**Problem**

How does the graph of $y = 2\left(\frac{1}{3}\right)^{x+1} - 4$ compare to the parent function $y = 2\left(\frac{1}{3}\right)^x$?

**Step 1** Determine the base of the function $y = 2\left(\frac{1}{3}\right)^x$. Because $b < 1$, the graph will represent exponential decay.

**Step 2** Make a table. Find more values if necessary to get a good picture of the graph.

| x | $y = 2\left(\frac{1}{3}\right)^x$ | y |
|---|---|---|
| −2 | $2\left(\frac{1}{3}\right)^{-2} = 2(9)$ | 18 |
| −1 | $2\left(\frac{1}{3}\right)^{-1} = 2(3)$ | 6 |
| 0 | $2\left(\frac{1}{3}\right)^0 = 2(1)$ | 2 |
| 1 | $2\left(\frac{1}{3}\right)^1 = 2\left(\frac{1}{3}\right)$ | $\frac{2}{3}$ |
| 2 | $2\left(\frac{1}{3}\right)^2 = 2\left(\frac{1}{9}\right)$ | $\frac{2}{9}$ |

**Step 3** Use the values for x and y from the table to graph the function.

**Step 4** For $y = 2\left(\frac{1}{3}\right)^{x+1} - 4$, $h = -1$ and $k = -4$. Shift the graph of the parent function above 1 unit left and 4 units down. The horizontal asymptote shifts down as well, from $y = 0$ to $y = -4$.

**Step 5** Use a graphing calculator to check your graph.

## page 20

### 7-2 Reteaching (continued)
Properties of Exponential Functions

For problems involving continuously compounded interest, use the following formula:

**Continuously Compounded Interest**
$A(t) = P \cdot e^{rt}$

A(t) is the amount in account after time t.
P is the principal.
r is the annual interest rate (as a decimal).
t is time (in years).

**Problem**

Suppose you invest $2000 at an annual interest rate of 5.5% compounded continuously. How much will you have in the account in 10 years?

**What do you know?**
principal P = $2000
interest rate r = 5.5% = 0.055
time t = 10 years

**Use the formula.**
$A(t) = P \cdot e^{rt}$
$= 2000 \cdot e^{(0.055)(10)}$
$= 2000 \cdot e^{0.55}$
$\approx 3466.50$

In ten years, you will have $3466.50.

**Exercises**
Graph each exponential function.

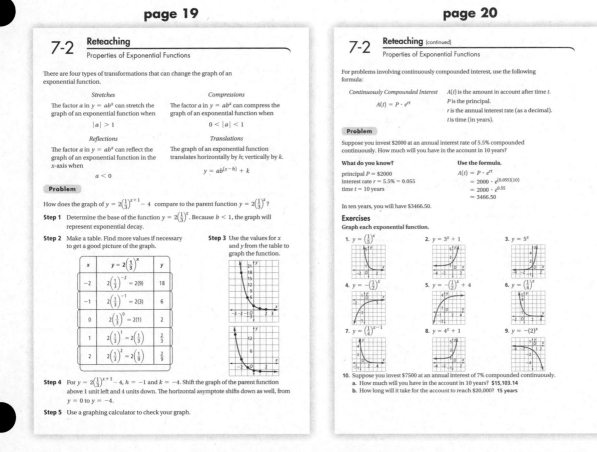

1. $y = \left(\frac{1}{5}\right)^x$   2. $y = 3^x + 1$   3. $y = 5^x$

4. $y = -\left(\frac{1}{2}\right)^x$   5. $y = -\left(\frac{1}{2}\right)^x + 4$   6. $y = \left(\frac{1}{4}\right)^x$

7. $y = \left(\frac{1}{4}\right)^{x-1}$   8. $y = 4^x + 1$   9. $y = -(2)^x$

10. Suppose you invest $7500 at an annual interest of 7% compounded continuously.
    a. How much will you have in the account in 10 years? **$15,103.14**
    b. How long will it take for the account to reach $20,000? **15 years**

## page 21

**7-3 ELL Support**
Logarithmic Functions as Inverses

For Exercises 1–3, draw a line from each word or phrase in Column A to the matching item in Column B.

Column A        Column B

1. logarithmic function    A. a logarithm with base 10

2. common logarithm    B. the inverse of an exponential function

3. logarithmic scale    C. uses the logarithm of a quantity instead of the quantity itself

For Exercises 4–9, draw a line from each word or phrase in Column A to the matching item in Column B.

Column A        Column B

4. parent function    A. $y = 0.75 \log_4 x$

5. stretch    B. $y = 5 \log_4 x$

6. compression    C. $y = \log_4 x - 3$

7. reflection in $x$-axis    D. $y = \log_4 x$

8. translation 3 units to the right    E. $y = -\log_4 x$

9. translation 3 units downward    F. $y = \log_4 (x - 3)$

## page 22

**7-3 Think About a Plan**
Logarithmic Functions as Inverses

**Chemistry** Find the concentration of hydrogen ions in seawater, if the pH level of seawater is 8.5.

**Understanding the Problem**

1. What is the pH of seawater? **8.5**

2. How do you represent the concentration of hydrogen ions? **$H^+$**

3. What is the problem asking you to determine?
   the concentration of hydrogen ions in seawater

**Planning the Solution**

4. Write the formula for the pH of a substance. **$pH = -\log[H^+]$**

5. Write an equation relating the pH of seawater to the concentration of hydrogen ions in seawater. **$8.5 = -\log[H^+]$**

**Getting an Answer**

6. Solve your equation to find the concentration of hydrogen ions in seawater.

$$8.5 = -\log[H^+]$$
$$-8.5 = \log[H^+]$$
$$10^{-8.5} = 10^{\log[H^+]}$$
$$10^{-8.5} = [H^+]$$
$$[H^+] = 10^{-8.5} \text{ or } 3.16 \times 10^{-9}$$

## page 23

**7-3 Practice**     *Form G*
Logarithmic Functions as Inverses

Write each equation in logarithmic form.

1. $9^2 = 81$
   $\log_9 81 = 2$

2. $\frac{1}{64} = \left(\frac{1}{4}\right)^3$
   $\log_{\frac{1}{4}} \left(\frac{1}{64}\right) = 3$

3. $8^3 = 512$
   $\log_8 512 = 3$

4. $\left(\frac{1}{3}\right)^{-2} = 9$
   $\log_{\frac{1}{3}} 9 = -2$

5. $2^9 = 512$
   $\log_2 512 = 9$

6. $4^5 = 1024$
   $\log_4 1024 = 5$

7. $5^4 = 625$
   $\log_5 625 = 4$

8. $10^{23} = 0.001$
   $\log_{10} 0.001 = -3$

Evaluate each logarithm.

9. $\log_2 128$  **7**

10. $\log_4 32$  $\frac{5}{2}$

11. $\log_9 (27)$  $\frac{3}{2}$

12. $\log_2 (-32)$  **undefined**

13. $\log_{\frac{1}{3}} \frac{1}{9}$  **2**

14. $\log 100{,}000$  **5**

15. $\log_7 7^6$  **6**

16. $\log_3 \frac{1}{81}$  **−4**

In 2004, an earthquake of magnitude 7.0 shook Papua, Indonesia. Compare the intensity level of that earthquake to the intensity level of each earthquake below.

17. magnitude 6.1 in Costa Rica, in 2009
   The Papua earthquake was about 8 times as strong as the Costa Rica earthquake.

18. magnitude 5.1 in Greece, in 2008
   The Papua earthquake was about 79 times as strong as the Greece earthquake.

19. magnitude 7.8 in the Fiji Islands, in 2007
   The Fiji Islands earthquake was about 6 times as strong as the Papua earthquake.

20. magnitude 8.3 in the Kuril Islands, in 2006
   The Kuril Islands earthquake was about 20 times as strong as the Papua earthquake.

Graph each logarithmic function.

21. $y = \log x$

22. $y = \log_3 x$

23. $y = \log_6 x$

## page 24

**7-3 Practice** (continued)     *Form G*
Logarithmic Functions as Inverses

Describe how the graph of each function compares with the graph of the parent function, $y = \log_b x$.

24. $y = \log_3 x - 2$  **translates 2 units down**

25. $y = \log_8 (x - 2)$  **translates 2 units to the right**

26. $y = \log_6 (x + 1) - 5$  **translates 1 unit to the left and 5 units down**

27. $y = \log_2 (x - 4) + 1$  **translates 4 units to the right and 1 unit up**

Write each equation in exponential form.

28. $\log_4 256 = 4$  $4^4 = 256$

29. $\log_7 1 = 0$  $7^0 = 1$

30. $\log_2 32 = 5$  $2^5 = 32$

31. $\log 10 = 1$  $10^1 = 10$

32. $\log_5 5 = 1$  $5^1 = 5$

33. $\log_8 \frac{1}{64} = -2$  $8^{-2} = \frac{1}{64}$

34. $\log_9 59{,}049 = 5$  $9^5 = 59{,}049$

35. $\log_{17} 289 = 2$  $17^2 = 289$

36. $\log_{56} 1 = 0$  $56^0 = 1$

37. $\log_{12} \frac{1}{144} = -2$  $12^{-2} = \frac{1}{144}$

38. $\log_2 \frac{1}{1024} = -10$  $2^{-10} = \frac{1}{1024}$

39. $\log_3 6561 = 8$  $3^8 = 6561$

40. A single-celled bacterium divides every hour. The number $N$ of bacteria after $t$ hours is given by the formula $\log_2 N = t$. After how many hours will there be 32 bacteria?  **5 hours**

For each pH given, find the concentration of hydrogen ions $[H^+]$. Use the formula $pH = -\log[H^+]$.

41. 7.2  $6.3 \times 10^{-8}$

42. 7.3  $5.0 \times 10^{-8}$

43. 8.2  $6.3 \times 10^{-9}$

44. 6.2  $6.3 \times 10^{-7}$

45. 5.6  $2.5 \times 10^{-6}$

46. 4.6  $2.5 \times 10^{-5}$

47. 7.0  $1.0 \times 10^{-7}$

48. 2.9  $1.3 \times 10^{-3}$

Find the inverse of each function.

49. $y = \log_2 x$  $y = 2^x$

50. $y = \log_{0.7} x$  $y = (0.7)^x$

51. $y = \log_{100} x$  $y = 10^{2x}$

52. $y = \log_8 x$  $y = 2^{3x}$

53. $y = \log_2 (4x)$  $y = 2^{x-2}$

54. $y = \log (x + 4)$  $y = 10^x - 4$

Find the domain and range of each function.

55. $y = \log_3 x - 2$
   domain: $x > 0$; range: all real numbers

56. $y = 2 \log_5 x$
   domain: $x > 0$; range: all real numbers

57. $y = \log (x + 1)$
   domain: $x > -1$; range: all real numbers

## page 25

**7-3** **Practice** *Form K*
Logarithmic Functions as Inverses

**Write each equation in logarithmic form.**

**1.** $32 = 2^5$ $\log_2 32 = 5$ **2.** $243 = 3^5$ $\log_3 243 = 5$ **3.** $625 = 5^4$ $\log_5 625 = 4$

**Write each equation in exponential form.**

**4.** $\log_3 9 = 2$ $9 = 3^2$ **5.** $\log_5 125 = 3$ $125 = 5^3$ **6.** $\log_8 512 = 3$ $512 = 8^3$

**Evaluate each logarithm.**

**7.** $\log_9 27$ **8.** $\log_8 256$ $\frac{8}{3}$ **9.** $\log_{125} \frac{1}{25}$ $-\frac{2}{3}$

$\log_9 27 = x$ $\log_8 256 = x$
$27 = 9^x$ $256 = 8^x$
$3^3 = (3^2)^x$
$3^3 = 3^{2x}$
$3 = 2x$
$x = \frac{3}{2}$

The formula $\log \frac{I_1}{I_2} = M_1 - M_2$ is used to compare the intensity levels of earthquakes. The variable $I$ is the intensity measured by a seismograph. The variable $M$ is the measurement on the Richter scale. Use the formula to answer the following problem.

**10.** In 1906, an earthquake of magnitude 8.25 hit San Francisco, California. Indonesia was hit by an earthquake of magnitude 8.5 in 1938. Compare the intensity of the two earthquakes. The earthquake in Indonesia was approximately 1.78 times more intense than the earthquake in San Francisco.

## page 26

**7-3** **Practice** (continued) *Form K*
Logarithmic Functions as Inverses

**11. Error Analysis** A student drew the graph below to represent the function $y = \log_4 x$. What mistake did the student make when she drew her graph? She did not reflect the graph across the line $y = x$.

**Graph each logarithmic function.**

**12.** $y = \log_2 x$ **13.** $y = \log_{\frac{1}{3}} x$

**Identify each function as a compression, a stretch, or a translation of the parent function.**

**14.** $y = 4\log_4 x$ stretch **15.** $y = \log_2 x + 10$ translation **16.** $y = 0.25\log_4 x$ compression

**Transform the function $y = \log_5 x$ as indicated below.**

**17.** stretch by a factor of 3 and translate 6 units up $y = 3\log_5 x + 6$

**18.** compress by a factor of 0.4 and reflect in the $x$-axis $y = -0.4\log_5 x$

## page 27

**7-3** **Standardized Test Prep**
Logarithmic Functions as Inverses

**Multiple Choice**

**For Exercises 1–4, choose the correct letter.**

**1.** Which of the following is the logarithmic form of the equation $4^{-3} = \frac{1}{64}$? C

Ⓐ $\log_{-3}\left(\frac{1}{64}\right) = 4$      Ⓒ $\log_4\left(\frac{1}{64}\right) = -3$

Ⓑ $\log_{-3} 4 = \frac{1}{64}$      Ⓓ $\log_{\frac{1}{64}} 4 = -3$

**2.** What is the value of $\log_2 8$? I

Ⓕ 64      Ⓗ 16

Ⓖ 8      Ⓘ 3

**3.** How does the graph of $y = \log_5 (x - 3)$ compare with the graph of the parent function, $y = \log_5 x$? C

Ⓐ translated 3 units to the left      Ⓒ translated 3 units to the right

Ⓑ translated 3 units down      Ⓓ translated 3 units up

**4.** In 2009, an earthquake of magnitude 6.7 shook the Kermadec Islands off the coast of New Zealand. Also in 2009, an earthquake of magnitude 5.1 occurred in the Alaska Peninsula. How many times stronger was the Kermadec earthquake than the Alaska earthquake? F

Ⓕ 39.811      Ⓗ 5.77

Ⓖ 20.593      Ⓘ 0.025

**Short Response**

**5.** A single-celled bacterium divides every hour. The number $N$ of bacteria after $t$ hours is given by the formula $\log_2 N = t$.
**a.** After how many hours will there be 64 bacteria?
**b.** Explain in words or show work for how you determined the number of hours.

[2] a. 6 hours
b. $\log_2 N = t$ can be written in the exponential form $2^t = N$. Substituting 64 for $N$, the equation becomes $2^t = 64$. Rewriting 64 with base 2, the equation becomes $2^t = 2^6$. Since the bases are equal, $t = 6$.
[1] incorrect exponential form OR incorrect explanation
[0] incorrect answers and no explanation OR no answers given

## page 28

**7-3** **Enrichment**
Logarithmic Functions as Inverses

**Log Jams**
The logarithm is a tool originally developed and used to aid in calculations, yet this viewpoint of logarithms is not the only one of interest. Logarithms are also useful when thought of as real-valued functions, or as inverse functions of the corresponding exponential functions. The idea of a logarithm as an inverse function of an exponential function means that $\log_b x$ is a question to be answered. For example, you can read the expression $\log_2 8$ as "what exponent on base 2 gives 8?" The answer is 3, because $2^3 = 8$.

Thinking of a logarithm as an exponent helps to order some logarithms without evaluating them. For example, the logarithms $\log_7 8$, $\log_7 7$, and $\log_7 6$ are in descending order since the exponent needed on base 7 that gives 8 would be greater than 1, and 1 is in turn greater than the exponent needed on base 7 that gives 6.

You can also compose logarithms as you would compose other functions, where their domain and ranges agree. Thus, you evaluate $\log_4 (\log_5 25)$ by evaluating $\log_5 25 = 2$, then evaluating $\log_4 2 = \frac{1}{2}$.

**Rewrite each equation in exponential form to solve the equation.**

**1.** Solve for $x$: $\log_x 81 = 4$ 3

**2.** Solve for $x$: $\log_x 2 = 2$ $\sqrt{2}$

**3.** Which is greater, $\log_2 3$ or $\log_3 2$? $\log_2 3$ is greater

**4.** Solve for $x$: $\log_3 x = \log_x 3$ $\frac{1}{3}$, 3

**5.** Which is greater, $\frac{1}{3}$ of $\log_4 2$ or $\frac{1}{2}$ of $\log 10$? $\frac{1}{2} \log 10$ is greater

**6.** Solve for $x$: $\log_2 (\log_2 x) = 2$ 16

**7.** Which is greater, $\frac{1}{3} \log_2 (\log_3 8.5)$ or $\frac{1}{2} \log_3 (\log_2 8.5)$? $\frac{1}{2} \log_3 (\log_2 8.5)$ is greater

**8.** Which of the following are equal? $\log \frac{1}{2}$ and $\log 1 - \log 2$ are equal

$\log \frac{1}{2}$      $\frac{\log 1}{\log 2}$      $\log 1 - \log 2$

**Rewrite in exponential form and solve for $x$.**

**9.** $\log_5 1 = x$ 0      **10.** $\log_2 (2x^2 - 7) = 0$ $-2, 2$

**11.** $\log_x 7 = 1$ 7      **12.** $\log_2 x^2 = 2$ $\pm 2$

**13.** $\log_3 1 = x$ 0      **14.** $\log_{17} 17 = x$ 1

**15.** $\log_x 3^4 = 1$ 81      **16.** $\log_3 x = 0$ 1

**17.** $\log_3 3^2 = x$ 2      **18.** $\log_4 (x + 1) = 0$ 0

**19.** $1 + \log_6 (x - 1) = 1$ 2      **20.** $-1 + \log x = -1$ 1

## page 29

### 7-3 Reteaching
Logarithmic Functions as Inverses

A logarithmic function is the inverse of an exponential function.

To evaluate logarithmic expressions, use the fact that $x = \log_b y$ is the same as $y = b^x$. Keep in mind that $x = \log y$ is another way of writing $x = \log_{10} y$.

**Problem**

What is the logarithmic form of $6^3 = 216$?

**Step 1** Determine which equation to use.

The equation is in the form $b^x = y$.

**Step 2** Find $x$, $y$, and $b$.

$b = 6$, $x = 3$, and $y = 216$

**Step 3** Because $y = b^x$ is the same as $x = \log_b y$, rewrite the equation in logarithmic form by substituting for $x$, $y$, and $b$.

$3 = \log_6 216$

**Exercises**

Write each equation in logarithmic form.

1. $4^{-3} = \frac{1}{64}$
   $\log_4 \frac{1}{64} = -3$

2. $5^{-2} = \frac{1}{25}$
   $\log_5 \frac{1}{25} = -2$

3. $8^{-1} = \frac{1}{8}$
   $\log_8 \frac{1}{8} = -1$

4. $11^0 = 1$
   $\log_{11} 1 = 0$

5. $6^1 = 6$
   $\log_6 6 = 1$

6. $6^{-3} = \frac{1}{216}$
   $\log_6 \frac{1}{216} = -3$

7. $17^0 = 1$
   $\log_{17} 1 = 0$

8. $17^1 = 17$
   $\log_{17} 17 = 1$

**Problem**

What is the exponential form of $4 = \log_5 625$?

**Step 1** Determine which equation to use.

The equation is in the form $x = \log_b y$.

**Step 2** Find $x$, $y$, and $b$.

$x = 4$, $b = 5$, and $y = 625$

**Step 3** Because $x = \log_b y$ is the same as $y = b^x$, rewrite the equation in exponential form by substituting for $x$, $y$, and $b$.

$625 = 5^4$

## page 30

### 7-3 Reteaching (continued)
Logarithmic Functions as Inverses

**Exercises**

Write each equation in exponential form.

9. $3 = \log_2 8$   $2^3 = 8$

10. $2 = \log_5 25$   $5^2 = 25$

11. $\log 0.1 = -1$   $10^{-1} = -0.1$

12. $\log 7 \approx 0.845$   $10^{0.845} \approx 7$

13. $\log 1000 = 3$   $10^3 = 1000$

14. $-2 = \log 0.01$   $10^{-2} = 0.01$

15. $\log_3 81 = 4$   $3^4 = 81$

16. $\log_{49} 7 = \frac{1}{2}$   $49^{\frac{1}{2}} = 7$

17. $\log_8 \frac{1}{4} = -\frac{2}{3}$   $8^{-\frac{2}{3}} = \frac{1}{4}$

18. $\log_2 128 = 7$   $2^7 = 128$

19. $\log_5 \frac{1}{625} = -4$   $5^{-4} = \frac{1}{625}$

20. $\log_6 36 = 2$   $6^2 = 36$

**Problem**

What is the value of $\log_4 32$?

$x = \log_4 32$   Write the equation in logarithmic form $x = \log_b y$.

$32 = 4^x$   Rewrite in exponential form $y = b^x$.

$2^5 = (2^2)^x$   Rewrite each side of the equation with like bases in order to solve the equation.

$2^5 = 2^{2x}$   Simplify.

$5 = 2x$   Set the exponents equal to each other.

$x = \frac{5}{2}$   Solve for $x$.

$\log_4 32 = \frac{5}{2}$

**Exercises**

Evaluate the logarithm.

21. $\log_2 64$   6

22. $\log_4 64$   3

23. $\log_3 3^4$   4

24. $\log 10$   1

25. $\log 0.1$   $-1$

26. $\log 1$   0

27. $\log_8 2$   $\frac{1}{3}$

28. $\log_{32} 2$   $\frac{1}{5}$

29. $\log_9 3$   $\frac{1}{2}$

## page 31

### 7-4 ELL Support
Properties of Logarithms

| Product Property | Quotient Property | Power Property |
|---|---|---|
| $\log_b mn = \log_b m + \log_b n$ | $\log_b \frac{m}{n} = \log_b m - \log_b n$ | $\log_b m^n = n \log_b m$ |
| **Example:** | **Example:** | **Example:** |
| $\log_4 (4 \cdot 3) = \log_4 4 + \log_4 3$ | $\log_3 \frac{12}{5} = \log_3 12 - \log_3 5$ | $\log_5 7^3 = 3 \log_5 7$ |

Identify the property that is demonstrated by each equation.

1. $\log_4 \frac{7}{3} = \log_4 7 - \log_4 3$   __quotient property__

2. $\log_3 6^5 = 5 \log_3 6$   __power property__

3. $\log_7 \frac{15}{4} = \log_7 15 - \log_7 4$   __quotient property__

4. $\log_5 (6 \cdot 4) = \log_5 6 + \log_5 4$   __product property__

5. $\log_4 12^5 = 5 \log_4 12$   __power property__

Identify the values of the symbols in the equations below.

6. $\log_4 \left( 8 \cdot \square \right) = \log_4 \lozenge + \log_4 6$   $\square = \underline{6}$   $\lozenge = \underline{8}$

7. $\log_3 \frac{15}{\square} = \log_3 \lozenge - \log_3 2$   $\square = \underline{2}$   $\lozenge = \underline{15}$

8. $\log_5 \square^3 = \lozenge \log_5 6$   $\square = \underline{6}$   $\lozenge = \underline{3}$

Write each expression as a single logarithm.

9. $\log_6 6 - \log_6 2 = \underline{\log_6 \frac{6}{2}}$

10. $\log_6 5 + \log_6 3 = \underline{\log_6 (5 \cdot 3)}$

## page 32

### 7-4 Think About a Plan
Properties of Logarithms

**Construction** The foreman of a construction team puts up a sound barrier that reduces the intensity of the noise by 50%. By how many decibels is the noise reduced? Use the formula $L = 10 \log \frac{I}{I_0}$ to measure loudness. (*Hint*: Find the difference between the expression for loudness for intensity $I$ and the expression for loudness for intensity $0.5I$.)

**Know**

1. You can represent the intensity of the original noise by   $\boxed{I}$.

2. You can represent the intensity of the reduced noise by   $\boxed{0.5I}$.

3. The formula for loudness is   $\boxed{L = 10\log \frac{I}{I_0}}$ .

**Need**

4. To solve the problem I need to find:

   the difference between the expression for the original noise intensity and the

   expression for the reduced noise intensity .

**Plan**

5. What is an expression for the loudness of the original construction noise?  $10\log \frac{I}{I_0}$

6. What is an expression for the loudness of the reduced construction noise?  $10\log \frac{0.5I}{I_0}$

7. Use your expressions to find the difference between the loudness of the original construction noise and the loudness of the reduced construction noise.

   $10\log \frac{I}{I_0} - 10\log \frac{0.5I}{I_0} = 10\left(\log \frac{I}{I_0} - \log \frac{0.5I}{I_0}\right) = 10\log \frac{I}{0.5I} = 10\log \frac{1}{0.5} = 10\log 2 \approx 3$

8. The sound barrier reduced the loudness by   $\boxed{3 \text{ dB}}$.

## page 33

**7-4** **Practice** Form G
Properties of Logarithms

**Write each expression as a single logarithm.**

1. $\log_5 4 + \log_5 3$
$\log_5 12$

2. $\log_6 25 - \log_6 5$
$\log_6 5$

3. $\log_2 4 + \log_2 2 - \log_2 8$
$\log_2 1 = 0$

4. $5\log_7 x - 2\log_7 x$
$\log_7 x^3$

5. $\log_4 60 - \log_4 4 + \log_4 x$
$\log_4 15x$

6. $\log 7 - \log 3 + \log 6$
$\log 14$

7. $2\log x - 3\log y$
$\log \frac{x^2}{y^3}$

8. $\frac{1}{2}\log r + \frac{1}{3}\log s - \frac{1}{4}\log t$
$\log \frac{r^{\frac{1}{2}} s^{\frac{1}{3}}}{t^{\frac{1}{4}}}$

9. $\log_3 4x + 2\log_3 5y$
$\log_3 100xy^2$

10. $5\log 2 - 2\log 2$
$\log 8$

11. $\frac{1}{3}\log 3x + \frac{2}{3}\log 3x$
$\log 3x$

12. $2\log 4 + \log 2 + \log 2$
$\log 64$

13. $(\log 3 - \log 4) - \log 2$
$\log \frac{3}{8}$

14. $5\log x + 3\log x^2$
$\log x^{11}$

15. $\log_6 3 - \log_6 6$
$\log_6 \frac{1}{2}$

16. $\log 2 + \log 4 - \log 7$
$\log \frac{8}{7}$

17. $\log_3 2x - 5\log_3 y$
$\log_3 \frac{2x}{y^5}$

18. $\frac{1}{3}(\log_2 x - \log_2 y)$
$\log_2 \frac{x^{\frac{1}{3}}}{y^{\frac{1}{3}}}$

19. $\frac{1}{2}\log x + \frac{1}{3}\log y - 2\log z$
$\log \frac{x^{\frac{1}{2}} y^{\frac{1}{3}}}{z^2}$

20. $3(4\log t^2)$
$\log t^{24}$

21. $\log_5 y - 4(\log_5 r + 2\log_5 t)$
$\log_5 \frac{y}{r^4 t^8}$

**Expand each logarithm. Simplify if possible.**

22. $\log xyz$
$\log x + \log y + \log z$

23. $\log \frac{x}{yz}$
$\log x - \log y - \log z$

24. $\log 6x^3 y$
$\log 6 + 3\log x + \log y$

25. $\log 7(3x - 2)^2$
$\log 7 - 2\log (3x - 2)$

26. $\log \sqrt{\frac{2rst}{5w}}$
$\frac{1}{2}\log s + \frac{1}{2}\log t - \frac{1}{2}\log w$

27. $\log \frac{5x}{4y}$
$\log 2 + \frac{1}{2}\log r +$ $\log 5 + \log x - \log 4 - \log y$

28. $\log_5 5x^{-5}$
$\log_5 5 - 5\log_5 x$, or $1 - 5\log_5 x$

29. $\log \frac{2x^2 y}{3k^3}$
$\log 2 + 2\log x +$ $\log y - \log 3 - 3\log k$

30. $\log_4 (3xyz)^2$
$2\log_4 3 +$ $2\log_4 x + 2\log_4 y + 2\log_4 z$

**Use the Change of Base Formula to evaluate each expression. Round your answer to the nearest thousandth.**

31. $\log_4 32$  2.5

32. $\log_3 5$  1.465

33. $\log_2 15$  3.907

34. $\log_6 17$  1.581

35. $\log_6 10$  1.285

36. $\log_5 6$  1.113

37. $\log_8 1$  0

38. $\log_9 11$  1.091

39. The concentration of hydrogen ions in a batch of homemade ketchup is $10^{-4}$. What is the pH level of the ketchup?  4

## page 34

**7-4** **Practice** (continued) Form G
Properties of Logarithms

**Determine if each statement is true or false. Justify your answer.**

40. $\log 12 = \log 4 + \log 3$
true; $\log 12 = \log (3 \cdot 4) = \log 4 + \log 3$

41. $\log \frac{3}{5} = \frac{\log 3}{\log 5}$
false; $\log \frac{3}{5} = \log 3 - \log 5 \neq \frac{\log 3}{\log 5}$

42. $\log_6 12 + \log_6 3 = 2$
true; $\log_6 12 + \log_6 3 = \log_6 36 = 2$

43. $\frac{1}{2}\log_4 4x = \log_4 2x$
false; $\frac{1}{2}\log_4 4x = \log_4 (4x)^{\frac{1}{2}} = \log_4 2x^{\frac{1}{2}} \neq \log_4 2x$

**Use the properties of logarithms to evaluate each expression.**

44. $\log_2 8 - \log_2 4$  1

45. $\log_2 160 - \log_2 5$  5

46. $\log_6 27 + \log_6 8$  3

47. $\log_7 14 - \log_7 2$  1

48. $\log_4 64 + 2\log_4 2$  4

49. $\frac{1}{4}\log_3 162 - \log_3 \sqrt[4]{2}$  1

**State the property or properties used to rewrite each expression.**

50. $\log 6 - \log 3 = \log 2$
Quotient Prop.

51. $6\log 2 = \log 64$
Power Prop.

52. $\log 3x = \log 3 + \log x$
Product Prop.

53. $\frac{1}{3}\log_2 x = \log_2 \sqrt[3]{x}$
Power Prop.

54. $\frac{2}{3}\log 7 = \log \sqrt[3]{49}$
Power Prop.

55. $\log_4 20 - 3\log_4 x = \log_4 \frac{20}{x^3}$
Power and Quotient Prop.

The formula for loudness in decibels (dB) is $L = 10\log \frac{I}{I_0}$, where $I$ is the intensity of a sound in watts per square meter (W/m$^2$) and $I_0$ is $10^{-12}$ W/m$^2$, the intensity of a barely audible sound.

56. A sound has an intensity of $5.92 \times 10^{25}$ W/m$^2$. What is the loudness of the sound in decibels? Use $I_0 = 10^{-12}$ W/m$^2$.  about 377.7 decibels

57. Suppose you decrease the intensity of a sound by 45%. By how many decibels would the loudness be decreased?  about 2.6 decibels

58. **Writing** Explain why $\log \left(\frac{9}{4}\right) \neq \frac{\log 9}{\log 4}$.  $\log \left(\frac{9}{4}\right) = \log 9 - \log 4 \neq \frac{\log 9}{\log 4}$

## page 35

**7-4** **Practice** Form K
Properties of Logarithms

| Properties of Logarithms | | |
|---|---|---|
| **Product Property** | **Quotient Property** | **Power Property** |
| $\log_b mn = \log_b m + \log_b n$ | $\log_b \frac{m}{n} = \log_b m - \log_b n$ | $\log_b m^n = n\log_b m$ |

**Write each expression as a single logarithm.**

1. $\log_3 9 + \log_3 24$  $\log_3 216$

2. $\log_4 16^3$  $3\log_4 16$

3. $\log_2 7 - \log_2 9$  $\log_2 \frac{7}{9}$

4. $\log_3 8^5$  $5\log_3 8$

5. $\log_4 x - \log_4 y$  $\log_4 \frac{x}{y}$

6. $\log 5 + \log 7$  $\log 35$

**Expand each logarithm. Simplify if possible.**

7. $\log_3 27x$  $\log_3 27 + \log_3 x$

8. $\log \frac{3}{7}$  $\log 3 - \log 7$

9. $\log_4 y^2 z^3$  $2\log_4 y + 3\log_4 z$

10. $\log_5 \frac{3^2}{x}$
$2\log_5 3 - \log_5 x$

11. $\log_3 15xy$
$1 + \log_3 5 + \log_3 x + \log_3 y$

12. $\log 8xz^4$
$3\log 2 + \log x + 4\log z$

13. **Open-Ended** Write three different logarithms. You should be able to expand each logarithm by one of the properties of logarithms. Answers may vary.
Sample: $\log_5 6x$, $\log \frac{3}{4}$, $\log_3 7^2$

## page 36

**7-4** **Practice** (continued) Form K
Properties of Logarithms

| Change of Base Formula |
|---|
| For any positive numbers $m$, $b$, and $c$, with $b \neq 1$ and $c \neq 1$, |
| $$\log_b m = \frac{\log_c m}{\log_c b}$$ |

**Use the Change of Base Formula to evaluate each expression.**

14. $\log_{32} 4$
$\frac{\log_2 4}{\log_2 32} = \frac{2}{5} = 0.4$

15. $\log_9 27$  1.5

16. $\log_4 12$  about 1.792

17. **Error Analysis** Your friend used the Change of Base Formula to evaluate the expression $\log_4 8$. Her answer was $\frac{2}{3}$. What error did your friend make? What is the correct answer?
Sample answer: Your friend confused the numerator and the denominator in the formula. The correct answer is $\frac{3}{2}$.

**Use the following formula to solve Exercise 18.**

| Formula for Loudness of a Sound (decibels) |
|---|
| $$L = 10\log \frac{I}{I_0}$$ |

- $I$ is the intensity of a sound in watts per square meter (W/m$^2$).
- $I_0$ is the intensity of a sound that can barely be heard.
- $I_0 = 10^{-12}$ W/m$^2$

18. Your classmate went to a rock concert. At the loudest point during the concert, the sound had an intensity of $2.35 \times 10^{-3}$ W/m$^2$. What was the loudness of this sound in decibels?
about 93.71 decibels

## page 37

### 7-4 Standardized Test Prep
Properties of Logarithms

**Multiple Choice**

For Exercises 1–4, choose the correct letter.

1. Which statement correctly demonstrates the Power Property of Logarithms? **D**

   Ⓐ $\frac{1}{2}\log_5 9 = \log_5 81$   Ⓒ $\frac{1}{2}\log_5 9 = \log_5 18$

   Ⓑ $\frac{1}{2}\log_5 9 = \log_5 \frac{9}{2}$   Ⓓ $\frac{1}{2}\log_5 9 = \log_5 3$

2. Which expression is the correct expansion of $\log_4 (3x)^2$? **G**

   Ⓕ $\frac{1}{2}(\log_4 3 - \log_4 x)$   Ⓗ $2(\log_4 3 - \log_4 x)$

   Ⓖ $2(\log_4 3 + \log_4 x)$   Ⓘ $2\log_4 3 + \log_4 x$

3. Which expression is equivalent to $\log_7 16$? **C**

   Ⓐ $\frac{\log_7 16}{\log 10}$   Ⓒ $\frac{\log 16}{\log 7}$

   Ⓑ $\frac{\log_{16} 10}{\log_7 10}$   Ⓓ $\frac{\log 7}{\log 16}$

4. Which statement correctly expresses $4\log_3 x + 7\log_3 y$ as a single logarithm? **F**

   Ⓕ $\log_3 x^4 y^7$   Ⓗ $\log_3 (x^4 + y^7)$

   Ⓖ $\log_3 (4x + 7y)$   Ⓘ $\log_3 (4x - 7y)$

**Short Response**

5. The pH of a substance equals $-\log[\text{H}^+]$, where $[\text{H}^+]$ is the concentration of hydrogen ions. The concentration of hydrogen ions in pure water is $10^{-7}$ and the concentration of hydrogen ions in a sodium hydroxide solution is $10^{-14}$.
   a. Without using a calculator, what is the difference of the pH levels of pure water and the sodium hydroxide solution?
   b. Explain in words or show work for how you determined the difference of the pH levels.

   [2] a. $-7$
   b. $\text{pH} = -\log[\text{H}^+]$, $\Delta\text{pH} = -\log[\text{H}^+_w] - (-\log[\text{H}^+_s]) = \log[\text{H}^+_s] - \log[\text{H}^+_w]$
   $= \log[10^{-14}] - \log[10^{-7}] = -14\log 10 - (-7\log 10) = -14(1) + 7(1) = -7$
   The pH of pure water is 7 less than the pH of the sodium hydroxide solution.
   [1] incorrect equation form OR incorrect explanation
   [0] incorrect answers and no work shown OR no answers given

## page 38

### 7-4 Enrichment
Properties of Logarithms

Scotsman John Napier and Joost Burgi from Switzerland are credited for being the first to introduce the concept of a logarithm. While the logarithm they described is quite different than the one we use today, both men used logarithms to simplify mathematical calculations. Arithmetic operations of addition and subtraction are relatively easy to compute, but without the modern calculator, multiplication and division of powers and roots can be time-consuming. Before calculators, logarithms were used to simplify an expression to an addition or subtraction problem. The logarithm values could be found in extensive tables and the calculations were more easily completed.

1. Consider the relation $y = \dfrac{x^{\frac{3}{4}}\sqrt{x^3}}{(3x+2)^5}$ as an example. Without using a calculator, determine the value for $y$ when $x = 16$. $\frac{512}{312,500,000} = \frac{16}{9,765,625}$

2. While the calculations in Exercise 1 are not impossible, they are certainly time-consuming and, with roots involved, are inaccurate. If you take the log base 10 of both sides, the equation becomes $\log y = \log\dfrac{x^{\frac{3}{4}}\sqrt{x^3}}{(3x+2)^5}$. Rewrite the right side of the equation using the log properties.
   $\log y = \frac{3}{4}\log x + \frac{3}{2}\log x - 5\log(3x+2)$

To evaluate a logarithmic equation like the one above, the values were found in a table and the arithmetic calculations were completed. To get a sense of how this was done, assume you have a table of values for logarithms using base $a$. In this table you find that $\log_a 2 = 0.301$, $\log_a 3 = 0.477$, and $\log_a 5 = 0.699$.

3. Use logarithm properties to rewrite $\log_a 30$ using the three log values given. Then evaluate your expression. $\log_a 30 = \log_a (2)(3)(5) = \log_a 2 + \log_a 3 + \log_a 5$; 1.477

4. Use logarithm properties to rewrite $\log_a 50$ and evaluate your expression.
   $\log_a 50 = \log_a (2)(5^2) = \log_a 2 + 2\log_a 5$; 1.699

5. Use logarithm properties to rewrite $\log_a 12.5$ and evaluate your expression.
   $\log_a (12.5) = \log_a \left(\frac{5^2}{2}\right) = 2\log_a 5 - \log_a 2$; 1.097

## page 39

### 7-4 Reteaching
Properties of Logarithms

You can write a logarithmic expression containing more than one logarithm as a single logarithm as long as the bases are equal. You can write a logarithm that contains a number raised to a power as a logarithm with the power as a coefficient. To understand the following properties, remember that logarithms are powers.

| Name | Formula | Why? |
|---|---|---|
| Product Property | $\log_b mn = \log_b m + \log_b n$ | When you multiply two powers, you add the exponents. Example: $2^6 \cdot 2^2 = 2^{(6+2)} = 2^8$ |
| Quotient Property | $\log_b \frac{m}{n} = \log_b m + \log_b n$ | When you divide two powers, you subtract the exponents. Example: $\frac{2^6}{2^2} = 2^{(6-2)} = 2^4$ |
| Power Property | $\log_b m^n = n\log_b m$ | When you raise a power to a power, you multiply the exponents. Example: $(2^6)^2 = 2^{(6 \cdot 2)} = 2^{12}$ |

**Problem**

What is $2\log_2 6 - \log_2 9 + \frac{1}{3}\log_2 27$ written as a single logarithm?

$2\log_2 6 - \log_2 9 + \frac{1}{3}\log_2 27 = \log_2 6^2 - \log_2 9 + \log_2 27^{\frac{1}{3}}$   Use the Power Property twice.

$= \log_2 36 - \log_2 9 + \log_2 3$   $6^2 = 36$, $27^{\frac{1}{3}} = \sqrt[3]{27} = 3$

$= (\log_2 36 - \log_2 9) + \log_2 3$   Group two of the logarithms. Use order of operations.

$= \log_2 \frac{36}{9} + \log_2 3$   Quotient Property

$= \log_2 \left(\frac{36}{9} \cdot 3\right)$   Product Property

$= \log_2 12$   Simplify.

As a single logarithm, $2\log_2 6 - \log_2 9 + \frac{1}{3}\log_2 27 = \log_2 12$.

## page 40

### 7-4 Reteaching (continued)
Properties of Logarithms

To evaluate logarithms with any base, you can rewrite the logarithm as a quotient of two logarithms with the same base.

Move the base to the bottom.   $\log_b m = \dfrac{\log_c m}{\log_c b}$   Move the number to the numerator.

**Problem**

What is $\log_4 8$ written as a quotient of two logarithms with base 2? Simplify your answer, if possible.

$\log_4 8 = \dfrac{\log_2 8}{\log_2 4}$   The base is 4 and the number is 8. Move the base to the bottom and the number to the numerator.

$= \dfrac{3}{2}$   Evaluate the logarithms in the numerator and the denominator.

**Exercises**

Write each logarithmic expression as a single logarithm.

1. $\log_3 13 + \log_3 3$ **$\log_3 39$**   2. $2\log x + \log 5$ **$\log 5x^2$**   3. $\log_4 2 - \log_4 6$ **$\log_4 \frac{1}{3}$**

4. $3\log_3 3 - \log_3 3$ **$\log_3 9$, or 2**   5. $\log_5 8 + \log_5 x$ **$\log_5 8x$**   6. $\log 2 - 2\log x$ **$\log \frac{2}{x^2}$**

7. $\log_2 x + \log_2 y$ **$\log_2 xy$**   8. $3\log_7 x - 5\log_7 y$ **$\log_7 \frac{x^3}{y^5}$**   9. $4\log x + 3\log x$ **$\log x^7$**

10. $\log_5 x + 3\log_5 y$ **$\log_5 xy^3$**   11. $3\log_2 x - \log_2 y$ **$\log_2 \frac{x^3}{y}$**   12. $\log_2 16 - \log_2 8$ **$\log_2 2$, or 1**

Write each logarithm as a quotient of two common logarithms. Simplify your answer, if possible. (*Hint:* Common logarithms are logarithms with base 10.)

13. $\log_4 12$ **$\frac{\log 12}{\log 4}$**   14. $\log_2 1000$ **$\frac{3}{\log 2}$**   15. $\log_5 16$ **$\frac{\log 16}{\log 5}$**

16. $\log_{11} 205$ **$\frac{\log 205}{\log 11}$**   17. $\log_9 32$ **$\frac{\log 32}{\log 9}$**   18. $\log_{100} 51$ **$\frac{\log 51}{2}$**

## page 41

### 7-5 ELL Support
Exponential and Logarithmic Equations

There are two sets of cards below that show how to solve the equation $\log_6 (x - 1) + \log_6 x = 1$. The set on the left explains the thinking. The set on the right shows the steps. Write the thinking and the steps in the correct order.

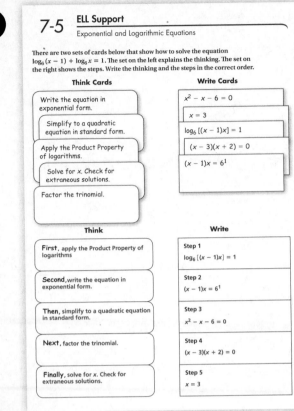

**Think Cards**

Write the equation in exponential form.

Simplify to a quadratic equation in standard form.

Apply the Product Property of logarithms.

Solve for x. Check for extraneous solutions.

Factor the trinomial.

**Write Cards**

$x^2 - x - 6 = 0$

$x = 3$

$\log_6 [(x - 1)x] = 1$

$(x - 3)(x + 2) = 0$

$(x - 1)x = 6^1$

**Think**

**First**, apply the Product Property of logarithms

**Second**, write the equation in exponential form.

**Then**, simplify to a quadratic equation in standard form.

**Next**, factor the trinomial.

**Finally**, solve for x. Check for extraneous solutions.

**Write**

Step 1
$\log_6 [(x - 1)x] = 1$

Step 2
$(x - 1)x = 6^1$

Step 3
$x^2 - x - 6 = 0$

Step 4
$(x - 3)(x + 2) = 0$

Step 5
$x = 3$

## page 42

### 7-5 Think About a Plan
Exponential and Logarithmic Equations

**Seismology** An earthquake of magnitude 7.6 occurred in 2001 in Gujarat, India. It was 251 times as strong as the greatest earthquake ever to hit Pennsylvania. What is the magnitude of the Pennsylvania earthquake? (*Hint:* Refer to the Richter scale on page 453.)

**Know**

1. The magnitude of the Gujarat earthquake is $\boxed{7.6}$.

2. The ratio of the intensity of the Gujarat earthquake to the intensity of Pennsylvania's greatest earthquake is $\boxed{251}$.

**Need**

3. To solve the problem I need to find:
   the magnitude of the greatest Pennsylvania earthquake

**Plan**

4. Let $I_1$ and $M_1$ be the intensity and magnitude of the Gujarat earthquake. Let $I_2$ and $M_2$ be the intensity and magnitude of Pennsylvania's greatest earthquake. What equation should you use to model this situation?
   $\log \frac{I_1}{I_2} = M_1 - M_2$

5. What does $\frac{I_1}{I_2}$ represent? the ratio of the intensity of the Gujarat earthquake to the intensity of Pennsylvania's greatest earthquake

6. What can you substitute for $\frac{I_1}{I_2}$ in your equation? **251**

7. Solve your equation for the magnitude of Pennsylvania's greatest earthquake.
   $M_2 = M_1 - \log \frac{I_1}{I_2} = 7.6 - \log 251 \approx 5.2$

8. The magnitude of Pennsylvania's greatest earthquake was $\boxed{\text{about 5.2}}$.

## page 43

### 7-5 Practice
Exponential and Logarithmic Equations
*Form G*

Solve each equation.

1. $8^{2x} = 32$  **$\frac{5}{6}$**
2. $7^n = 343$  **3**
3. $9^{2x} = 27$  **$\frac{3}{4}$**
4. $25^{2n+1} = 625$  **$\frac{1}{2}$**
5. $36^{-2x+1} = 216$  **$-\frac{1}{4}$**
6. $64^x = 4096$  **2**

Solve each equation. Round answers to the nearest hundredth.

7. $5^{2x} = 20$  **0.93**
8. $8^{n+1} = 3$  **−0.47**
9. $4^{n-2} = 3$  **2.79**
10. $4^{3n} = 5$  **0.39**
11. $15^{2n-3} = 245$  **2.52**
12. $4^x - 5 = 12$  **2.04**

Solve by graphing. Round to the nearest hundredth.

13. $2^{n+5} = 120$  **1.91**
14. $5^{n+1} = 175$  **2.21**
15. $8^x = 58$  **1.95**
16. $10^n = 3$  **0.48**
17. $10^{3y} = 5$  **0.23**
18. $10^{k-2} = 20$  **3.30**
19. $5^x = 4$  **0.86**
20. $2^{4x} = 8$  **0.75**
21. $3^{x+5} = 15$  **−2.54**

Use a table to solve each equation. Round to the nearest hundredth.

22. $8^{2n} = 3$  **0.26**
23. $12^{2n-1} = 64$  **1.34**
24. $12^{n-2} = 8$  **2.84**
25. $10^x = 182$  **2.26**
26. $8^n = 12$  **1.19**
27. $10^{2x} = 9$  **0.48**
28. $5^{n+1} = 3$  **−0.32**
29. $10^{n-2} = 0.3$  **1.48**
30. $3^{3n} = 50$  **1.19**

31. The equation $y = 281(1.01)^x$ is a model for the population of the United States $y$, in millions of people, $x$ years after the year 2000. Estimate when the United States population will reach 400 million people.  **in the year 2035**

Solve each equation. Check your answers.

32. $\log x = 2$  **100**
33. $\log 4x = -1$  **$\frac{1}{40}$**
34. $\log 3x = 2$  **$\frac{100}{3}$**
35. $\log 4x = 2$  **25**
36. $4 \log x = 4$  **10**
37. $8 \log x = 16$  **100**
38. $2 \log x = 2$  **10**
39. $\log (2x + 5) = 3$  **$\frac{995}{2}$**
40. $\log (3x - 2) = 3$  **334**
41. $\log (x - 25) = 2$  **125**
42. $2 \log (2x + 5) = 4$  **$\frac{95}{2}$**
43. $3 \log (1 - 2x) = 6$  **$-\frac{99}{2}$**

## page 44

### 7-5 Practice (continued)
Exponential and Logarithmic Equations
*Form G*

Solve each equation.

44. $\log x - \log 4 = 3$  **4000**
45. $\log x - \log 4 = -2$  **$\frac{1}{25}$**
46. $2 \log x - \log 4 = 2$  **20**
47. $\log 3x - \log 5 = 1$  **$\frac{50}{3}$**
48. $2 \log x - \log 3 = 1$  **$\sqrt{30}$**
49. $\log 8 - \log 2x = -1$  **40**
50. $2 \log 3x - \log 9 = 1$  **$\sqrt{10}$**
51. $2 \log x - \log 5 = -2$  **$\frac{\sqrt{20}}{20}$**
52. $\log (x + 21) + \log x = 2$  **4**

53. The function $y = 1000(1.005)^x$ models the value of $1000 deposited at an interest rate of 6% per year (0.005 per month) $x$ months after the money is deposited.
    a. Use a graph (on your graphing calculator) to predict how many months it will be until the account is worth $1100.  **about 19 months**
    b. Predict how many years it will be until the account is worth $5000.  **about 27 years**

54. Suppose the population of a country is currently 8,100,000. Studies show this country's population is increasing 2% each year.
    a. What exponential function would be a good model for this country's population?  **$y = 8,100,000(1.02)^x$**
    b. Using the equation you found in part (a), how many years will it take for the country's population to reach 9 million? Round your answer to the nearest hundredth.  **5.32 years**

55. Suppose you deposit $2500 in a savings account that pays you 5% interest per year.
    a. How many years will it take for you to double your money?  **about 14 years**
    b. How many years will it take for your account to reach $8,000?  **about 24 years**

**Mental Math** Solve each equation.

56. $5^x = \frac{1}{25}$  **−2**
57. $4^x = 64$  **3**
58. $10^x = 0.0001$  **−4**
59. $\log_3 81 = x$  **4**
60. $\log_2 \frac{1}{32} = x$  **−5**
61. $\log 1,000,000 = x$  **6**

Use the properties of exponential and logarithmic functions to solve each system. Check your answers.

62. $\begin{cases} -2^{10-x} + y = 0 \\ y = 8^{x+2} \end{cases}$  **(1, 512)**
63. $\begin{cases} 3^{2x-y} = 1 \\ 4^{x+y} - 8 = 0 \end{cases}$  **$\left(\frac{1}{2}, 1\right)$**
64. $\begin{cases} \log_2 (x - 2y) = 3 \\ \log_2 (x + y) = \log_2 8 \end{cases}$  **(8, 0)**

## page 45

**7-5** Practice                                                      Form K
Exponential and Logarithmic Equations

Solve each equation. To start, rewrite each side with a common base.

**1.** $125^{2x} = 25$
$(5^3)^{2x} = 5^2$
$5^{6x} = 5^2$
$6x = 2$
$x = \frac{1}{3}$

**2.** $2^{3x-3} = 64$
$2^{3x-3} = 2^6$
$x = 3$

**3.** $81^{3x} = 27$
$x = \frac{1}{4}$

Solve each equation. Round to the nearest ten-thousandth. Check your answers.
To start, take the logarithm of each side.

**4.** $6^{4x} = 234$
$\log 6^{4x} = \log 234$
$4x \log 6 = \log 234$
$x = \frac{\log 234}{4 \log 6}$
$x \approx 0.7612$

**5.** $3^{5x} = 375$
$\log 3^{5x} = \log 375$
$x = 1.0790$

**6.** $7^{3x} - 24 = 184$
$x = 0.9143$

**Graphing Calculator** Solve by graphing. Round to the nearest ten-thousandth.

**7.** $3^{6x} = 2000$
Let $Y_1 = 3^{6x}$ and $Y_2 = 2000$.  $x \approx 1.1531$

**8.** $8^{3x} = 154$  $x \approx 0.8074$

**9.** $12^{4x} = 4600$  $x \approx 0.8485$

Use the following formula for Exercise 10.

$$T(m) = a(1 + r)^m$$

• $m$ = the number of minutes it takes for $\frac{3}{4}$ of the crowd to leave the stadium
• $T(m)$ = the number of people in the stadium after $m$ minutes
• $a$ = the number of people currently in the stadium
• $r$ = the percent change in the number of people in the stadium

**10.** There are currently 100,000 people in a stadium watching a soccer game. When the game ends, about 3% of the crowd will leave the stadium each minute. At this rate, how many minutes will it take for $\frac{3}{4}$ of the crowd to leave the stadium? **about 47 minutes**

## page 46

**7-5** Practice (continued)                                          Form K
Exponential and Logarithmic Equations

Convert from Logarithmic Form to Exponential Form to solve each equation.

| Exponential and Logarithmic Form | |
| --- | --- |
| Logarithmic Form $\log_b x = y$ | Exponential Form $b^y = x$ |

**11.** $\log (2x + 4) = 3$
$2x + 4 = 10^3$
$2x = 996$
$x = 498$

**12.** $\log 4z - 3 = 2$
$\log 4z = 5$
$z = 25,000$

**13.** $\log (2x - 8) = 2$
$x = 54$

Use the properties of logarithms to solve each equation.

| Product Property | Quotient Property | Power Property |
| --- | --- | --- |
| $\log_b mn = \log_b m + \log_b n$ | $\log_b \frac{m}{n} = \log_b m - \log_b n$ | $\log_b m^n = n \log_b m$ |

**14.** $2 \log x + \log 4 = 3$
$\log x^2 + \log 4 = 3$
$\log 4x^2 = 3$
$4x^2 = 10^3$
$x^2 = 250$
$x \approx 15.81$

**15.** $\log y - \log 4 = 2$
$\log \frac{y}{4} = 2$
$y = 400$

**16.** $\log 10 + \log 2x = 3$
$x = 50$

**17. Error Analysis** Your friend used the following steps to solve the equation $\log x + \log 6 = 4$. What error did he make? What is the correct answer?

$\log x + \log 6 = 4$
$\log \frac{x}{6} = 4$
$\frac{x}{6} = 10^4$
$x = 6000$

He applied the Quotient Property rather than the Product Property; $x = \frac{5000}{3}$.

## page 47

**7-5** Standardized Test Prep
Exponential and Logarithmic Equations

**Multiple Choice**

For Exercises 1–5, choose the correct letter.

**1.** If $9^x = 243$, what is the value of $x$? **C**
Ⓐ 2   Ⓑ 5   Ⓒ 2.5   Ⓓ 10

**2.** If $2^{3x+2} = 64$, what is the value of $x$? **G**
Ⓕ $\frac{8}{3}$   Ⓖ $\frac{4}{3}$   Ⓗ 2   Ⓘ $\frac{3}{4}$

**3.** If $\log (3x + 25) = 2$, what is the value of $x$? **A**
Ⓐ 25   Ⓑ 75   Ⓒ $41\frac{2}{3}$   Ⓓ 100

**4.** Which best approximates the solution of $16^{2x} = 124$? **F**
Ⓕ 0.869   Ⓖ 1.150   Ⓗ 1.739   Ⓘ 3.477

**5.** Which equation represents the solution of $2^{3x+1} = 7$? **D**
Ⓐ $x = 3\left(\frac{\log 7}{\log 2} - 1\right)$
Ⓒ $x = \frac{1}{3}\left(\frac{\log 2}{\log 7} - 1\right)$
Ⓑ $x = \frac{\log 7}{3 \log 2} - 1$
Ⓓ $x = \frac{1}{3}\left(\frac{\log 7}{\log 2} - 1\right)$

**Short Response**

**6.** In 2007, the population of Tallahassee, Florida was 168,979. Some researchers believe that the population of Tallahassee will increase at a rate of 1% each year for the 10 years following this.
 **a.** If the researchers are correct, how many years will it take for the population of Tallahassee to reach 180,000?
 **b.** Explain in words or show your work for how you determined the number of years found in part (a).
 **[2] a.** about 7 years
    **b.** Because the population grows at a constant rate each year, an exponential model of the situation is $y = 168,979(1.01)^x$. $180,000 = 168,979(1.01)^x \rightarrow$
    $\frac{180,000}{168,979} = 1.01^x \rightarrow \log 1.0652 = x \log 1.01 \rightarrow x = \frac{\log 1.0652}{\log 1.01} \approx 6.348$.
 **[1]** incorrect number of years OR incorrect explanation
 **[0]** incorrect answers and no work shown OR no answers given

## page 48

**7-5** Enrichment
Exponential and Logarithmic Equations

When solving logarithm equations, you primarily use the Product Property, Quotient Property, and Power Property to simplify the equation. Here is an interesting, lesser-known property of logarithms to explore.

**1.** Determine the value of each pair of expressions.
 $\log_2 4, \log_4 2$  $2, \frac{1}{2}$
 $\log_3 81, \log_{81} 3$  $4, \frac{1}{4}$
 $\log_{10} 1000, \log_{1000} 10$  $3, \frac{1}{3}$

**2.** How are the values of each pair of expressions related?
 Answers may vary. Sample: When the base and argument are switched, the expressions are reciprocals.

**3.** This reciprocal property states that $\log_a b = \frac{1}{\log_b a}$. To prove this property, assume $r = \log_a b$ and $s = \log_b a$. Rewrite each of these equations in exponential form.  $a^r = b, b^s = a$

**4.** Next, use one equation to substitute an equivalent expression in for $a$. What is your new equation?  $(b^s)^r = b$

**5.** Use the laws of exponents to simplify.  $b^{sr} = b$

**6.** Because the bases are the same, what equation can you write for the exponents?  $sr = 1$

**7.** What must be true about $s$ and $r$ if the product equals 1?  $s$ and $r$ must be reciprocals.

**8.** Use this new property to solve the equation $\log_5 x + \frac{1}{\log_x 5} = 4$.  25

## page 49

**7-5** Reteaching
Exponential and Logarithmic Equations

Use logarithms to solve exponential equations.

**Problem**

What is the solution of $7 - 5^{2x-1} = 4$?

| | |
|---|---|
| $7 - 5^{2x-1} = 4$ | |
| $-5^{2x-1} = -3$ | First isolate the term that has the variable in the exponent. Begin by subtracting 7 from each side. |
| $5^{2x-1} = 3$ | Multiply each side by $-1$. |
| $\log_5 5^{2x-1} = \log_5 3$ | Because the variable is in the exponent, use logarithms. Take $\log_5$ of each side because 5 is the base of the exponent. |
| $(2x - 1)\log_5 5 = \log_5 3$ | Use the Power Property of Logarithms. |
| $2x - 1 = \log_5 3$ | Simplify. (Recall that $\log_b b = 1$.) |
| $2x - 1 = \dfrac{\log 3}{\log 5}$ | Apply the Change of Base Formula. |
| $2x = \dfrac{\log 3}{\log 5} + 1$ | Add 1 to each side. |
| $x = \dfrac{1}{2}\left(\dfrac{\log 3}{\log 5} + 1\right)$ | Divide each side by 2. |
| $x \approx 0.84$ | Use a calculator to find a decimal approximation. |

**Exercises**

Solve each equation. Round the answer to the nearest hundredth.

**1.** $2^x = 5$  2.32
**2.** $10^{2x} = 8$  0.45
**3.** $5^{x+1} = 25$  1
**4.** $2^{x+3} = 9$  0.17
**5.** $3^{2x-3} = 7$  2.39
**6.** $4^x - 5 = 3$  1.50
**7.** $5 + 2^{x+6} = 9$  $-4$
**8.** $4^{3x} + 2 = 3$  0
**9.** $1 - 3^{2x} = -5$  0.82
**10.** $2^{3x} - 2 = 13$  1.30
**11.** $5^{2x+7} - 1 = 8$  $-2.82$
**12.** $7 - 2^{x+7} = 5$  $-6$

## page 50

**7-5** Reteaching (continued)
Exponential and Logarithmic Equations

Use exponents to solve logarithmic equations.

**Problem**

What is the solution of $8 - \log(4x - 3) = 4$?

| | |
|---|---|
| $8 - \log(4x - 3) = 4$ | |
| $-\log(4x - 3) = -4$ | First isolate the term that has the variable in the logarithm. Begin by subtracting 8 from each side. |
| $\log(4x - 3) = 4$ | Multiply each side by $-1$. |
| $4x - 3 = 10^4$ | Write in exponential form. |
| $4x - 3 = 10,000$ | Simplify. |
| $4x = 10,003$ | Add 3 to each side. |
| $x = \dfrac{10,003}{4}$ | Solve for $x$. |
| $x = 2500.75$ | Divide. |

**Exercises**

Solve each equation. Round the answer to the nearest thousandth.

**13.** $\log x = 2$  100
**14.** $\log 3x = 3$  333.333
**15.** $\log 2x + 2 = 6$  5000
**16.** $5 + \log(2x + 1) = 6$  4.5
**17.** $\log 5x + 62 = 62$  0.2
**18.** $6 - \log \frac{1}{2}x = 3$  2000
**19.** $\log(4x - 3) + 6 = 4$  0.753
**20.** $\frac{2}{3}\log 5x = 2$  200
**21.** $2\log 250x - 6 = 4$  400
**22.** $5 - 2\log x = \frac{1}{2}$  177.828

## page 51

**7-6** ELL Support
Natural Logarithms

**Problem**

What is the solution of the equation $3e^{4x} + 5 = 26$? Explain your work and check your solution.

| | |
|---|---|
| $3e^{4x} + 5 = 26$ | Write the original equation. |
| $3e^{4x} = 21$ | Subtract 5 from each side. |
| $e^{4x} = 7$ | Divide each side by 3. |
| $4x = \ln 7$ | Rewrite in logarithmic form. |
| $x = 0.25\ln 7$ | Divide each side by 4. |
| $x \approx 0.486$ | Use a calculator. |

**Check** 
| | |
|---|---|
| $3e^{4x} + 5 = 26$ | Write the original equation. |
| $3e^{4(0.486)} + 5 = 26$ | Substitute 0.486 for $x$. |
| $25.96 \approx 26$ | Use a calculator. |

**Exercise**

What is the solution of the equation $5e^{2x} - 2 = 12$? Explain your work and check your solution.

| | |
|---|---|
| $5e^{2x} - 2 = 12$ | Write the original equation. |
| $5e^{2x} = 14$ | Add 2 to each side. |
| $e^{2x} = 2.8$ | Divide each side by 5. |
| $2x = \ln 2.8$ | Write in logarithmic form. |
| $x = 0.5\ln 2.8$ | Divide each side by 2. |
| $x \approx 0.515$ | Use a calculator. |

**Check** 
| | |
|---|---|
| $5e^{2x} - 2 = 12$ | Write the original equation. |
| $5e^{2(0.515)} - 2 = 12$ | Substitute 0.515 for $x$. |
| $12.005 \approx 12$ | Use a calculator. |

## page 52

**7-6** Think About a Plan
Natural Logarithms

**Archaeology** A fossil bone contains 25% of its original carbon-14. What is the approximate age of the bone?

**Understanding the Problem**

1. What is the amount of carbon-14 remaining in the fossil bone?
   25% of the original amount

2. If $a$ is the amount of carbon-14 originally in an object and $t$ is the object's age in years, what equation gives the amount of carbon-14 in the object?  $y = ae^{-0.00012t}$

3. What is the problem asking you to determine?
   the approximate age of the fossil bone

**Planning the Solution**

4. What number should you substitute for $y$ in the equation above?  $0.25a$

5. Write an equation you can use to determine the approximate age of the bone.  $0.25a = ae^{-0.00012t}$

**Getting an Answer**

6. How can logarithms help you solve your equation?
   After dividing each side by $a$, take the natural log of both sides of the equation
   to eliminate $e$.

7. Solve your equation to find the approximate age of the bone.
   $0.25a = ae^{-0.00012t}$
   $0.25 = e^{-0.00012t}$
   $\ln(0.25) = \ln\left(e^{-0.00012t}\right)$
   $\ln(0.25) = -0.00012t$
   $t = \frac{\ln(0.25)}{-0.00012} \approx 11,552$ years

## page 53

**7-6** **Practice** Form G
Natural Logarithms

**Write each expression as a single natural logarithm.**

1. $\ln 16 - \ln 8$ **ln 2**

2. $2\ln 3 + \ln 9$ **ln 243**

3. $a\ln 4 - \ln b$ $\ln \frac{4^a}{b}$

4. $\ln z - 3\ln x$ $\ln \frac{z}{x^3}$

5. $\frac{1}{2}\ln 9 + \ln 3x$ **ln 9x**

6. $4\ln x + 3\ln y$ $\ln x^4 y^3$

7. $\frac{1}{3}\ln 8 + \ln x$ **ln 2x**

8. $3\ln a - b\ln 2$ $\ln \frac{a^3}{2^b}$

9. $2\ln 4 - \ln 8$ **ln 2**

**Solve each equation. Check your answers. Round your answer to the nearest hundredth.**

10. $4\ln x = -2$ **0.61**

11. $2\ln(3x - 4) = 7$ **12.37**

12. $5\ln(4x - 6) = -6$ **1.58**

13. $-7 + \ln 2x = 4$ **29,937.07**

14. $3 - 4\ln(8x + 1) = 12$ **−0.11**

15. $\ln x + \ln 3x = 14$ **633.14**

16. $2\ln x + \ln x^2 = 3$ **2.12**

17. $\ln x + \ln 4 = 2$ **1.85**

18. $\ln x - \ln 5 = -1$ **1.84**

19. $\ln e^x = 3$ **3**

20. $3\ln e^{2x} = 12$ **2**

21. $\ln e^{x+5} = 17$ **12**

22. $\ln 3x + \ln 2x = 3$ **1.83**

23. $5\ln(3x - 2) = 15$ **7.36**

24. $7\ln(2x + 5) = 8$ **−0.93**

25. $\ln(3x + 4) = 5$ **48.14**

26. $\ln \frac{2x}{41} = 2$ **151.48**

27. $\ln(2x - 1)^2 = 4$ **4.19**

**Use natural logarithms to solve each equation. Round your answer to the nearest hundredth.**

28. $e^x = 15$ **2.71**

29. $4e^x = 10$ **0.92**

30. $e^{x+2} = 50$ **1.91**

31. $4e^{3x-1} = 5$ **0.41**

32. $e^{x-4} = 2$ **4.69**

33. $5e^{6x+3} = 0.1$ **−1.15**

34. $e^x = 1$ **0**

35. $e^{\frac{x}{5}} = 32$ **17.33**

36. $3e^{3x-5} = 49$ **2.60**

37. $7e^{5x+8} = 0.23$ **−2.28**

38. $6 - e^{12x} = 5.2$ **−0.02**

39. $e^{\frac{x}{2}} = 25$ **6.44**

40. $e^{2x} = 25$ **1.61**

41. $e^{\ln 5x} = 20$ **4**

42. $e^{\ln x} = 21$ **21**

43. $e^{x+6} + 5 = 1$ **no solution**

## page 54

**7-6** **Practice** (continued) Form G
Natural Logarithms

The formula $P = 50e^{-\frac{t}{25}}$ gives the power output $P$, in watts, needed to run a certain satellite for $t$ days. Find how long a satellite with the given power output will operate.

44. 10 W **about 40.2 days**

45. 12 W **about 35.7 days**

46. 14 W **about 31.8 days**

The formula for the maximum velocity $v$ of a rocket is $v = -0.0098t + c\ln R$, where $c$ is the exhaust velocity in km/s, $t$ is the firing time, and $R$ is the mass ratio of the rocket. A rocket must reach 7.7 km/s to attain a stable orbit 300 km above Earth.

47. What is the maximum velocity of a rocket with a mass ratio of 18, an exhaust velocity of 2.2 km/s, and a firing time of 25 s? **about 6.11 km/s**

48. Can the rocket in Exercise 47 achieve a stable orbit? Explain your answer.
No; the maximum velocity of 6.11 km/s is less than the 7.7 km/s needed for a stable orbit. Therefore, the spacecraft cannot attain a stable orbit 300 km above Earth.

49. What mass ratio would be needed to achieve a stable orbit for a rocket with an exhaust velocity of 2.5 km/s and a firing time of 29 s? **about 24.38**

50. A rocket with an exhaust velocity of 2.4 km/s and a 28 second firing time can reach a maximum velocity of 7.8 km/s. What is the mass ratio of the rocket?
**about 28.91**

By measuring the amount of carbon-14 in an object, a paleontologist can determine its approximate age. The amount of carbon-14 in an object is given by $y = ae^{-0.00012t}$, where $a$ is the amount of carbon-14 originally in the object, and $t$ is the age of the object in years.

51. A fossil of a bone contains 32% of its original carbon-14. What is the approximate age of the bone? **about 9495 years old**

52. A fossil of a bone contains 83% of its original carbon-14. What is the approximate age of the bone? **about 1553 years old**

**Simplify each expression.**

53. $\ln e^4$ **4**

54. $5\ln e^5$ **25**

55. $\frac{\ln e^2}{2}$ **1**

56. $\ln e^{100}$ **100**

## page 55

**7-6** **Practice** Form K
Natural Logarithms

**Write each expression as a single logarithm. The first expression is simplified for you.**

1. $\ln 3 + \ln 4$
$\ln(3 \cdot 4)$
$\ln 12$

2. $3\ln x - \ln 5$
$\ln x^3 - \ln 5$
$\ln \frac{x^3}{5}$

3. $(\ln 3x + \ln 4) - \ln 8$
$\ln \frac{3x}{2}$

**Solve each equation. Round your answers to the nearest tenth. The first equation is solved for you.**

4. $\ln(3x + 1) = 4$
$3x + 1 = e^4$
$3x = e^4 - 1$
$3x \approx 53.6$
$x \approx 17.9$

5. $\ln(y - 2) = 3$
$y - 2 = e^3$
$y \approx 22.1$

6. $3\ln 2x = 3$
$x \approx 1.4$

**Use the following formula to complete Exercises 7 and 8.**

| Maximum Velocity of a Rocket |
| --- |
| $v = -0.0098t + c\ln R$ |

- $v$ = maximum velocity
- $t$ = rocket's firing time
- $c$ = velocity of exhaust
- $R$ = mass ratio of the rocket

7. A rocket has a mass ratio of 24. The rocket's exhaust has a velocity of 2.4 km/s. The rocket's firing time is 32 seconds. Approximately what is the rocket's maximum velocity? Round to the nearest tenth. **v ≈ 7.3 km/s**

8. The rocket in Exercise 7 was changed to prepare it for a new mission. The new mass ratio is 26, and the new exhaust velocity is 2.3 km/s. Will these changes increase or decrease the rocket's maximum velocity? What is the difference between the maximum velocities?
The changes will decrease the maximum velocity. The difference is approximately 0.1 km/s.

## page 56

**7-6** **Practice** (continued) Form K
Natural Logarithms

**Solve each equation. Round your answers to the nearest thousandth.**

9. $2e^{4x} - 4 = 10$
$2e^{4x} = 14$
$e^{4x} = 7$
$4x = \ln 7$
$x = 0.25\ln 7$
$x \approx 0.486$

10. $e^{\frac{x}{2}} + 6 = 12$
$e^{\frac{x}{2}} = 6$
$\frac{x}{2} = \ln 6$
$x \approx 3.584$

11. $e^{x-2} = 28$
$x \approx 5.332$

12. $e^{\frac{x}{4}} - 3 = 21$
$x \approx 12.712$

13. $e^{x+2} + 4 = 17$
$x \approx 0.565$

14. $3e^{\frac{x}{2}} - 5 = 19$
$x \approx 4.159$

15. **Writing** Explain the steps you would follow to solve the equation $4e^{3x} + 6 = 30$. What is the answer? Answers may vary. Sample: First, subtract 6 from both sides. Then divide both sides by 4, creating the equation $e^{3x} = 6$. Next, rewrite the equation in logarithmic form as $3x = \ln 6$. Finally, use a calculator to evaluate ln 6 and to divide by 3. The answer is approximately 0.597.

**Use the following formula to complete Exercise 16.**

| Bacteria Culture Decline |
| --- |
| $H = \frac{1}{r}(\ln P - \ln A)$ |

- $H$ = number or hours
- $r$ = rate of decline
- $P$ = initial bacteria population
- $A$ = reduced bacteria population

16. A scientist tests an antibiotic that causes a rate of decline of 0.18. About how long will it take this antibiotic to shrink a population of 4000 bacteria to 300? Round your answer to the nearest hundredth. **about 14.39 h**

## page 57

**7-6 Standardized Test Prep**
Natural Logarithms

### Multiple Choice

For Exercises 1–4, choose the correct letter. Do not use a calculator.

1. What is $3 \ln 5 - \ln 2$ written as a single natural logarithm? **D**
   (A) $\ln 7.5$    (B) $\ln 27$    (C) $\ln\left(\frac{5}{2}\right)^3$    (D) $\ln 62.5$

2. What is the solution of $e^{x+1} = 13$? **G**
   (F) $x = \ln 13 + 1$   (G) $x = \ln 13 - 1$   (H) $x = \ln 13$   (I) $x = \ln 12$

3. What is the solution of $\ln(x - 2)^2 = 6$? **C**
   (A) $2 + e^3$    (B) $2 - e^3$    (C) $2 \pm e^3$    (D) $2 \pm e^6$

4. What is the solution of $e^{\frac{x}{2}+1} + 3 = 8$? **G**
   (F) $x = 2 \ln 5 - 1$   (G) $x = 2 \ln 5 - 2$   (H) $x = 2 \ln 4$   (I) $x = \frac{1}{2}(\ln 5 - 1)$

### Short Response

5. The maximum velocity $v$ of a rocket is $v = -0.0098t + c \ln R$. The rocket fires for $t$ seconds and the velocity of the exhaust is $c$ km/s. The ratio of the mass of the rocket filled with fuel to the mass of the rocket without fuel is $R$. A spacecraft can attain a stable orbit 300 km above Earth if it reaches a velocity of 7.7 km/s.
   a. What is the velocity of a spacecraft whose booster rocket has a mass ratio of 16, an exhaust velocity of 3.2 km/s, and a firing time of 40 s?
   b. Can this rocket attain a stable orbit 300 km above Earth? Explain in words or show work for how you determined your answer.

[2] a. 8.48 km/s
   b. Yes; the maximum velocity of 8.48 km/s is greater than the 7.7 km/s needed for a stable orbit. Therefore, the spacecraft can attain a stable orbit 300 km above the Earth.
[1] incorrect velocity OR incorrect explanation
[0] incorrect answers and no work shown OR no answers given

## page 58

**7-6 Enrichment**
Natural Logarithms

### Calculating Natural Logarithms

You can compute natural logarithms with

$$\ln x = \frac{(x - 1)^1}{1} - \frac{(x - 1)^2}{2} + \frac{(x - 1)^3}{3} - \frac{(x - 1)^4}{4} + \frac{(x - 1)^5}{5} - \cdots$$

where the pattern continues forever. Notice that there are actually three patterns involved as the terms progress.

1. What is the pattern of the signs?
   **The signs alternate as the terms progress beginning with a positive term.**

2. What is the pattern of the exponents?
   **The exponents increase by 1 as the terms progress beginning with 1.**

3. What is the pattern of the denominators?
   **The denominators increase by 1 as the terms progress beginning with 1.**

4. For $x = 1$, what is the sum of the series? **0**

5. Use a calculator to fill in the blanks in the following chart to four decimal places. Then compare your results with the value of $\ln x$ obtained directly.

|  | $x = 1.1$ | $x = 1.5$ |
|---|---|---|
| $\frac{(x-1)^1}{1}$ | 0.1000 | 0.5000 |
| $-\frac{(x-1)^2}{2}$ | −0.0050 | −0.1250 |
| Result | 0.0950 | 0.3750 |
| $+\frac{(x-1)^3}{3}$ | 0.0003 | 0.0417 |
| Result | 0.0953 | 0.4167 |
| $-\frac{(x-1)^4}{4}$ | 0.0000 | −0.0156 |
| Result | 0.0953 | 0.4011 |
| $+\frac{(x-1)^5}{5}$ | 0.0000 | 0.0063 |
| Result | 0.0953 | 0.4074 |
| $\ln x$ | 0.0953 | 0.4055 |

## page 59

**7-6 Reteaching**
Natural Logarithms

The **natural logarithmic function** is a logarithm with base $e$, an irrational number.

You can write the natural logarithmic function as $y = \log_e x$, but you usually write it as $y = \ln x$.

$y = e^x$ and $y = \ln x$ are inverses, so if $y = e^x$, then $x = \ln y$.

To solve a natural logarithm equation:
- If the term containing the variable is an exponential expression, rewrite the equation in logarithmic form.
- If term containing the variable is a logarithmic expression, rewrite the equation in exponential form.

**Problem**

What is the solution of $4e^{2x} - 2 = 3$?

**Step 1** Isolate the term containing the variable on one side of the equation.
$$4e^{2x} - 2 = 3$$
$$4e^{2x} = 5 \qquad \text{Add 2 to each side of the equation.}$$
$$e^{2x} = \frac{5}{4} \qquad \text{Divide each side of the equation by 4.}$$

**Step 2** Take the natural logarithm of each side of the equation.
$$\ln\left(e^{2x}\right) = \ln\left(\frac{5}{4}\right)$$
$$2x = \ln\left(\frac{5}{4}\right) \qquad \text{Definition of natural logarithm}$$

**Step 3** Solve for the variable.
$$x = \frac{\ln\left(\frac{5}{4}\right)}{2} \qquad \text{Divide each side of the equation by 2.}$$
$$x \approx 0.112 \qquad \text{Use a calculator.}$$

**Step 4** Check the solution.
$$4e^{2(0.112)} - 2 \overset{?}{=} 3$$
$$4e^{0.224} - 2 \overset{?}{=} 3$$
$$3.004 \approx 3$$
The solution is $x \approx 0.112$.

## page 60

**7-6 Reteaching** (continued)
Natural Logarithms

**Problem**

What is the solution of $\ln(t - 2)^2 + 1 = 6$? Round your answer to the nearest thousandth.

**Step 1** Isolate the term containing the variable on one side of the equation.
$$\ln(t - 2)^2 + 1 = 6$$
$$\ln(t - 2)^2 = 5 \qquad \text{Subtract 1 from each side of the equation.}$$

**Step 2** Raise each side of the equation to the base $e$.
$$e^{\ln(t-2)^2} = e^5$$
$$(t - 2)^2 = e^5 \qquad \text{Definition of natural logarithm}$$

**Step 3** Solve for the variable.
$$t - 2 = \pm e^{\frac{5}{2}} \qquad \text{Take the square root of each side of the equation.}$$
$$t = 2 \pm e^{\frac{5}{2}} \qquad \text{Add 2 to each side of the equation.}$$
$$t \approx 14.182 \text{ or } -10.182 \qquad \text{Use a calculator.}$$

**Step 4** Check the solution.
$$\ln(14.182 - 2)^2 \overset{?}{=} 5 \qquad \ln(-10.182 - 2)^2 \overset{?}{=} 5$$
$$4.9999 \approx 5 \qquad\qquad 4.9999 \approx 5$$
The solutions are $t \approx 14.182$ and $-10.182$.

### Exercises

Use natural logarithms to solve each equation. Round your answer to the nearest thousandth. Check your answers.

1. $2e^x = 4$   0.693
2. $e^{4x} = 25$   0.805
3. $e^x = 72$   4.277
4. $e^{3x} = 124$   1.607
5. $12e^{3x-2} = 8$   0.532
6. $\frac{1}{2}e^{6x} = 5$   0.384

Solve each equation. Round your answer to the nearest thousandth. Check your answers.

7. $\ln(x - 3) = 2$   10.389
8. $\ln 2t = 4$   27.299
9. $1 + \ln x^2 = 2$   ±1.649
10. $\ln(2x - 5) = 3$   12.543
11. $\frac{1}{3}\ln 2t = 1$   10.043
12. $\ln(t - 4)^2 + 2 = 5$   8.482, −0.482

## page 61

### Chapter 7 Quiz 1
Lessons 7-1 through 7-3                                    Form G

**Do you know HOW?**

1. For the function $y = 5^{(x-2)}$, identify the transformation of the parent function
$y = 5^x$.  translates the graph $y = 5^x$ two units to the right

Write each equation in logarithmic form.

2. $64 = 8^2$          3. $8 = 2^3$          4. $125 = 5^3$          5. $729 = 3^6$
$\log_8 64 = 2$       $\log_2 8 = 3$       $\log_5 125 = 3$       $\log_3 729 = 6$

Graph each function. Then find the domain, range, and y-intercept.

6. $y = 5^x - 2$          7. $y = 3(2)^x$          8. $y = \left(\frac{1}{2}\right)^x$

domain: all real numbers;   domain: all real numbers;   domain: all real numbers;
range: $y \geq -2$; y-intercept: −1   range: $y \geq 0$; y-intercept: 3   range: $y \geq 0$; y-intercept: 1

Evaluate each logarithm.

9. $\log_3 243$  5          10. $\log_5 625$  4          11. $\log_9 729$  3          12. $\log_4 256$  4

**Do you UNDERSTAND?**

13. **Error Analysis** A classmate says that $y = \left(\frac{3}{2}\right)^x$ represents exponential decay.
What is the student's mistake?
$b = \frac{3}{2}$, because $b > 1$, the function represents exponential growth.

14. **Writing** Explain how you would graph an exponential function.
Make a table of values, substituting values for x into the exponential function to find
its corresponding y values; plot these points in the coordinate plane; connect the points
with a smooth curve.

15. **Reasoning** Find the value of $\log_8 64$ without using a calculator. Justify your
answer.
2; Answers may vary. Sample: Write $\log_8 64$ as an equation $\log_8 64 = x$; rewrite in
exponential form $64 = 8^x$; rewrite each side using a common base $2^6 = (2^3)^x$;
solve for x: $6 = 3x$.

## page 62

### Chapter 7 Quiz 2
Lessons 7-4 through 7-6                                    Form G

**Do you know HOW?**

Solve each equation. Round your answer to the nearest hundredth.

1. $\ln 3x = 8$          2. $\frac{1}{2}\ln 5x = 4$          3. $\ln (x - 4) = 2$
993.65                   596.19                             11.39

Write each expression as a single logarithm.

4. $\log_5 3 + \log_5 6$          5. $\log_2 32 - \log_2 8$          6. $\frac{1}{2}\log_4 25 + \log_4 2$
$\log_5 18$                       $\log_2 4$                         $\log_4 10$

Solve each equation.

7. $4^x = 16$          8. $9^{y-3} = 81$          9. $\log_{\frac{1}{3}} x = 2$
$x = 2$               $y = 5$                    $x = 300$

Expand each logarithm.

10. $\log_4 \frac{m}{n}$          11. $\log_5 (x \cdot \sqrt[3]{y})$          12. $\log_3 \frac{x^4}{y^2}$
$\log_4 m - \log_4 n$       $\log_5 x + \frac{1}{3}\log_5 y$       $4\log_3 x - 2\log_3 y$

**Do you UNDERSTAND?**

13. **Vocabulary** What is an exponential equation?
An exponential equation is an equation where an exponent includes a variable.

14. **Open-Ended** Write log 27 as a sum or difference of two logarithms. Simplify if possible.
Answers may vary. Sample: log 27 = log 9 + log 3

15. **Vocabulary** What is the base of the natural logarithmic function $y = \ln x$?  $e$

16. **Reasoning** Explain how you could find the value of $\log_{16} 64$ without using a calculator?
Answers may vary. Sample: Find a common base that has powers equaling 16 and 64;
$2^4 = 16$ and $2^6 = 64$; Using the common base, apply the Change of Base Formula and
simplify; $\log_{16} 64 = \frac{\log_2 64}{\log_2 16} = \frac{\log_2 2^6}{\log_2 2^4} = \frac{6}{4} = \frac{3}{2}$

## page 63

### Chapter 7 Chapter Test
Form G

**Do you know HOW?**

Solve each equation.

1. $8 - 3^x = -1$  2          2. $\log_3 81 = x$  4          3. $\log x - \log 3 = 2$  300

4. You put $2000 into an account earning 4% interest compounded continuously.
Find the amount in the account at the end of 8 years.  $2754.25

Describe how the graph of each function is related to the graph of its
parent function.

5. $y = -2^x + 1$  The graph is the graph of $y = 2^x$ reflected across the x-axis and
shifted up 1 unit.

6. $y = 3^{x-4}$  The graph is the graph of $y = 3^x$ shifted right 4 units.

7. $y = 5^{x+1} - 2$  The graph is the graph of $y = 5^x$ shifted left 1 unit and down 2 units.

Evaluate each logarithm.

8. $\log_5 125$  3          9. $\log_{\frac{1}{4}} \frac{1}{4}$  2          10. $\log_3 729$  6

11. $\log_9 \frac{1}{3}$  $-\frac{1}{2}$          12. $\log_{\frac{1}{4}} 16$  −2          13. $\log_8 \frac{1}{256}$  $-\frac{8}{3}$

Write each equation in logarithmic form.

14. $7^3 = 343$  $\log_7 343 = 3$          15. $\left(\frac{2}{3}\right)^{-3} = \frac{27}{8}$  $\log_{\frac{2}{3}} \frac{27}{8} = -3$          16. $2^{-4} = 0.0625$  $\log_2 0.0625 = -4$

Write each logarithmic expression as a single logarithm.

17. $\log 2 + 3\log 1$          18. $\log a - \log ab$          19. $\frac{1}{3}(\log_4 x + \log_4 z)$
$\log 2$                       $\log_b \frac{1}{b}$ or $-\log b$       $\log_4 \sqrt[3]{xz}$

## page 64

### Chapter 7 Chapter Test (continued)
Form G

Use the Change of Base Formula to rewrite each expression using common
logarithms.

20. $\log_4 12$          21. $\log_2 5$          22. $\log_8 14$
$\frac{\log 12}{\log 4}$       $\frac{\log 5}{\log 2}$       $\frac{\log 14}{\log 8}$

23. A parent increases a child's allowance by 15% each year. If the allowance is $3
now, when will it reach $15?  in 12 years

24. A scientist notes that the number of bacteria in a colony is 50. Two hours later, she notes
that the number of bacteria has increased to 80. If this rate of growth continues, how
much more time will it take for the number of bacteria to reach 100?  about 0.95 hour

Graph each function.

25. $y = -3^x + 1$          26. $y = \log_5 x$          27. $y = \log (x + 1)$

**Do you UNDERSTAND?**

28. **Writing** Describe the effect of different values of $a$ on the function $y = ab^x$.
If $|a| > 1$, it will stretch the graph of $y = b^x$. If $0 < |a| < 1$, it will compress (shrink) the
graph of $y = b^x$. If $a < 0$, there will be a reflection over the x-axis.

29. **Vocabulary** State which property or properties need to be used to write each
expression as a single logarithm.
a. $\log_6 16 - \log_6 4$          b. $2\log_2 3 + \log_2 4$
Quotient Property                Product and Power Properties

30. **Reasoning** Identify each function as *linear, quadratic,* or *exponential.* Explain
your reasoning.
a. $y = 4(2)^x$  exponential; the variable is in the exponent.
b. $y = 6(x)^2 + 1$  quadratic; the variable is raised to the power of 2.

31. **Writing** Explain the difference between exponential growth and exponential decay.
Answers may vary. Sample: The value of $b$ is greater than 1 in exponential growth,
whereas the value of $b$ is between 0 and 1 in exponential decay. The values of $y$
increase as the values of $x$ increase in exponential growth. The values of $y$ decrease
as the values of $x$ increase in exponential decay.

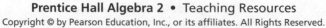

**Prentice Hall Algebra 2 • Teaching Resources**
Copyright © by Pearson Education, Inc., or its affiliates. All Rights Reserved.

## page 65

### Chapter 7 Quiz 1
Lessons 7–1 through 7–3

*Form K*

**Do you know HOW?**

Without graphing, determine whether the function represents exponential growth or decay.

**1.** $y = 2(1.05)^x$ **growth**   **2.** $y = 4\left(\frac{3}{5}\right)^x$ **decay**   **3.** $y = 3(0.45)^x$ **decay**

Identify the parent of each function. Then graph each function as a transformation of its parent function.

**4.** $y = 0.25 \cdot 4^x$  $y = 4^x$   **5.** $y = 2^{x-1} - 2$  $y = 2^x$

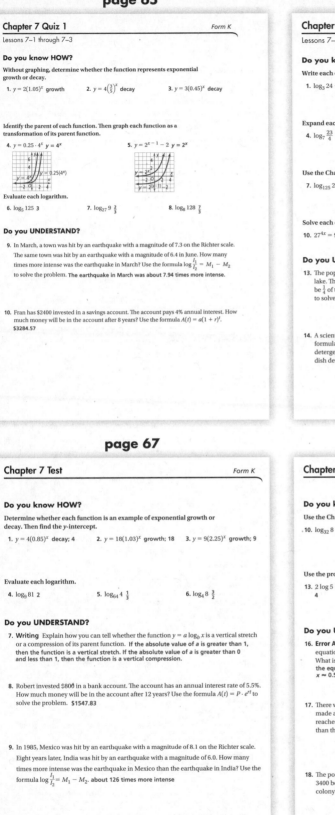

Evaluate each logarithm.

**6.** $\log_5 125$  **3**   **7.** $\log_{27} 9$  $\frac{2}{3}$   **8.** $\log_8 128$  $\frac{7}{3}$

**Do you UNDERSTAND?**

**9.** In March, a town was hit by an earthquake with a magnitude of 7.3 on the Richter scale. The same town was hit by an earthquake with a magnitude of 6.4 in June. How many times more intense was the earthquake in March? Use the formula $\log \frac{I_1}{I_2} = M_1 - M_2$ to solve the problem. **The earthquake in March was about 7.94 times more intense.**

**10.** Fran has $2400 invested in a savings account. The account pays 4% annual interest. How much money will be in the account after 8 years? Use the formula $A(t) = a(1 + r)^t$. **$3284.57**

## page 66

### Chapter 7 Quiz 2
Lessons 7–4 through 7–5

*Form K*

**Do you know HOW?**

Write each expression as a single logarithm.

**1.** $\log_3 24 + \log_3 2$  $\log_3 48$   **2.** $\log_2 12 - \log_2 3$  $\log_2 4$   **3.** $3\log x + 5\log y$  $\log x^3 y^5$

Expand each logarithm.

**4.** $\log_7 \frac{23}{4}$  $\log_7 23 - \log_7 4$   **5.** $\log_2 32x^3$  $3\log_2 x + 5$   **6.** $\log_6 \frac{x^4}{38}$  $4\log_6 x - \log_6 38$

Use the Change of Base Formula to evaluate each expression.

**7.** $\log_{125} 25$  $\frac{2}{3}$   **8.** $\log_7 25$  **about 1.65**   **9.** $\log_5 40$  **about 2.29**

Solve each equation.

**10.** $27^{4x} = 9$  $\frac{1}{6}$   **11.** $\log(6x - 2) = 3$  **167**   **12.** $\log 4 + \log x = 2$  **25**

**Do you UNDERSTAND?**

**13.** The population of fish in a lake is decreasing. There are currently 24,000 fish in the lake. The population is decreasing by 6% each year. In how many years will there be $\frac{1}{4}$ of the current number of fish in the lake? Use the formula $T(n) = a(1 + r)^n$ to solve the problem. **about 22 yr**

**14.** A scientist is calculating the pH levels of vinegar and dish detergent. He uses the formula $pH = -\log[H^+]$. $[H^+_v]$ for vinegar is $6.3 \times 10^{-3}$. $[H^+_d]$ for dish detergent is $10^{-12}$. What is the difference of the pH levels for vinegar and dish detergent? **about 9.8**

## page 67

### Chapter 7 Test
*Form K*

**Do you know HOW?**

Determine whether each function is an example of exponential growth or decay. Then find the *y*-intercept.

**1.** $y = 4(0.85)^x$  **decay; 4**   **2.** $y = 18(1.03)^x$  **growth; 18**   **3.** $y = 9(2.25)^x$  **growth; 9**

Evaluate each logarithm.

**4.** $\log_9 81$  **2**   **5.** $\log_{64} 4$  $\frac{1}{3}$   **6.** $\log_4 8$  $\frac{3}{2}$

**Do you UNDERSTAND?**

**7. Writing** Explain how you can tell whether the function $y = a\log_b x$ is a vertical stretch or a compression of its parent function. **If the absolute value of *a* is greater than 1, then the function is a vertical stretch. If the absolute value of *a* is greater than 0 and less than 1, then the function is a vertical compression.**

**8.** Robert invested $800 in a bank account. The account has an annual interest rate of 5.5%. How much money will be in the account after 12 years? Use the formula $A(t) = P \cdot e^{rt}$ to solve the problem. **$1547.83**

**9.** In 1985, Mexico was hit by an earthquake with a magnitude of 8.1 on the Richter scale. Eight years later, India was hit by an earthquake with a magnitude of 6.0. How many times more intense was the earthquake in Mexico than the earthquake in India? Use the formula $\log \frac{I_1}{I_2} = M_1 - M_2$. **about 126 times more intense**

## page 68

### Chapter 7 Test (continued)
*Form K*

**Do you know HOW?**

Use the Change of Base Formula to evaluate each expression.

**10.** $\log_{32} 8$  **0.6**   **11.** $\log_7 42$  **about 1.92**   **12.** $\log_{26} 5$  **about 0.49**

Use the properties of logarithms to solve the following logarithmic equations.

**13.** $2\log 5 + \log x = 2$  **4**   **14.** $\log(x - 21) + \log x = 2$  **25**   **15.** $\log 4x - \log 5 = 3$  **1250**

**Do you UNDERSTAND?**

**16. Error Analysis** A math test contained the equation $25^{2x} = 35$. A student used the equation $(5^2)^{2x} = 5^7$ to find his answer of $x = 1.75$. What error did the student make? What is the correct answer? **Sample answer: The student used a common base to solve the equation, but 25 and 35 do not have a common base. The correct answer is $x \approx 0.55$.**

**17.** There was a fireworks display in Downsville last night. The first burst during the display made a sound with an intensity of $3.14 \times 10^{-4}$ W/m². During the last burst, the sound reached an intensity of $4.25 \times 10^{-3}$ W/m². How many decibels louder was the last burst than the first burst? Use the formula $L = 10\log \frac{I}{I_0}$, where $I_0 = 10^{-12}$. **about 11 decibels**

**18.** The population of a bee colony is growing at a rate of 2.3% each year. There are currently 3400 bees in the colony. At this rate, in how many years will there be 10,200 bees in the colony? Use the formula $T(y) = a(1 + r)^y$ to solve the problem. **about 48.3 years**

## page 69

### Chapter 7 Performance Tasks

Give complete answers.

**Task 1**

a. Write an exponential function that could model the information in this graph.

b. Describe a business, scientific (not mathematical), or economic situation for what this graph might represent. Include how the different mathematical aspects of the graph affect the situation.

c. How will the graph and situation change when you change the base of this exponential function?

d. Describe the conditions under which the function represents a growth or decay situation.

Check students' work.

[4] Student writes an exponential function that models the information in the graph. Student writes a detailed explanation of what the graph might represent. Student includes significant information regarding how the exponential curve relates to the situation. Student includes examples of an exponential function that models growth and one that models decay.

[3] Student writes an exponential function that models the graph. Student describes a situation with minimal detail. There are minor errors in logic. Student includes concepts of exponential growth but does not relate the concepts to the situation.

[2] Student writes an exponential function with minor errors. The situation has detail, but with errors in logic. Student does not accurately describe the effect of changing the base, and cannot clearly distinguish between growth and decay.

[1] Student writes an exponential function that is only partially correct. Student creates a situation but does not include any detail or makes significant errors in logic.

[0] Student makes no attempt, or no response is given.

**Task 2**

a. Write a detailed description of how logarithms can be used to solve exponential equations and how exponents can be used to solve logarithmic equations.

b. Give and solve an example of each type of equation.

c. Explain why using logarithms and exponents to solve equations that contain the other is an important concept in mathematics.

Check students' work.

[4] Student writes a detailed explanation of how exponents and logarithms can be used to solve equations containing the other. Student gives appropriate and accurate examples and solves them correctly.

[3] Student writes a sufficient description of how exponents and logarithms can be used to solve equations containing the other. There are only minor errors in the examples and solutions that are provided.

[2] Student writes a limited description of how exponents and logarithms can be used to solve equations containing the other, with minor errors. There are major errors in the examples and solutions. Explanation on why this concept is important is missing or incorrect.

[1] Student writes a minimal amount of information about exponents and logarithms. There are major errors in logic. The examples lack sufficient detail.

[0] Student makes no attempt, or no response is given.

## page 70

### Chapter 7 Performance Tasks (continued)

**Task 3**

a. State the three Properties of Logarithms. $\log_b MN = \log_b M + \log_b N$; $\log_b \frac{M}{N} = \log_b M - \log_b N$; $\log_b M^x = x \log_b M$

b. Give an example for using each property. Check students' work.

c. Describe a real-life situation in which you would apply one or more of the properties. Show how you would use them. Check students' work.

[4] Student states all of the properties correctly and provides an accurate example of using each. Student clearly describes an appropriate real-life situation.

[3] Student states all of the properties correctly but makes minor errors in the examples. Description of real-life situation is slightly unclear.

[2] Student omits one or more properties but gives appropriate examples for the one(s) stated. Description of real-life situation involves logarithms but does not use the properties.

[1] Student states the properties but makes errors in the statement or the examples. Student neglects to describe a real-life situation.

[0] Student makes no attempt, or no response is given.

**Task 4**

a. What is the inverse of $f(x)$? $y = \ln x$

b. Graph the inverse function from part (a).

c. Rewrite the inverse function from part (a) in exponential form. $e^y = x$

d. Evaluate the inverse function from part (a) for $x = 1$ and $x = e$. 0; 1

[4] Student finds the inverse correctly. The graph is accurate. The inverse function is written in exponential form with no errors. There are no errors in calculations of values.

[3] Student finds the inverse correctly. Graph could be more accurate. Exponential form of the inverse function contains minor errors. There are minor errors in calculations.

[2] Student attempts to find the inverse correctly but makes minor errors. Graph, exponential form of the inverse, and calculations all have minor errors.

[1] Student does not find the inverse correctly. Graph contains major errors. There are major errors in calculations.

[0] Student makes no attempt, or no response is given.

## page 71

### Chapter 7 Cumulative Review

**Multiple Choice**

For Exercises 1–10, choose the correct letter.

1. Which of the following systems is *dependent*? C

  Ⓐ $\begin{cases} y = 2x - 1 \\ y = -2x + 2 \end{cases}$  Ⓑ $\begin{cases} y = 2x - 1 \\ y = 2x + 3 \end{cases}$  Ⓒ $\begin{cases} y = 2x - 1 \\ 2y = 4x - 2 \end{cases}$  Ⓓ $\begin{cases} y = 2x - 1 \\ y = -\frac{1}{2}x + 1 \end{cases}$

2. The electric current $I$ in amperes (A) of a circuit is given by the formula $\log_2 I = -t$. Find the current when $t$ is 3 s. G

  Ⓕ $-0.903$ A  Ⓖ $0.125$ A  Ⓗ $0.405$ A  Ⓘ $0.794$ A

3. Which of the following functions represent exponential growth? B

  Ⓐ $y = 50(0.50)^x$  Ⓑ $y = \frac{1}{2}(1.1)^x$  Ⓒ $y = 2\left(\frac{3}{8}\right)^x$  Ⓓ $y = 15(0.98)^x$

4. What is the next number in the pattern $1, -2, 4, -8, 16, \ldots$? F

  Ⓕ $-32$  Ⓖ $24$  Ⓗ $32$  Ⓘ $-24$

5. Use the Change of Base Formula to rewrite $\log_7 16$ using common logarithms. D

  Ⓐ $\frac{\log_7 16}{\log 10}$  Ⓑ $\frac{\log 7}{\log 16}$  Ⓒ $\frac{\log_{16} 10}{\log_{10} 7}$  Ⓓ $\frac{\log 16}{\log 7}$

6. Which of the following is the vertex of the function $y = -|2x| + 1$? H

  Ⓕ $(0, 2)$  Ⓖ $(2, 0)$  Ⓗ $(0, 1)$  Ⓘ $(1, 0)$

7. What is the simplified form of the expression $\sqrt[5]{x^{20} y^8}$? B

  Ⓐ $x^5 y^2$  Ⓑ $|x^5|y^2$  Ⓒ $x^5|y^2|$  Ⓓ $|x^5 y^2|$

8. Which of the following represents the polynomial $6x + 3x^2 - 2$ in standard form? G

  Ⓕ $-2 + 6x + 3x^2$  Ⓗ $-2 + 3x^2 + 6x$
  Ⓖ $3x^2 + 6x - 2$  Ⓘ $6x + 3x^2 - 2$

## page 72

### Chapter 7 Cumulative Review (continued)

9. Which of the following is $2 \ln 10 - \ln 5$ written as a single natural logarithm? D

  Ⓐ $\ln 2$  Ⓑ $\ln 4$  Ⓒ $\ln 15$  Ⓓ $\ln 20$

10. Which of the following is the correct expansion of $\log_6 \frac{x^2 y}{z^4}$? H

  Ⓕ $\log_6 2x + \log_6 y - \log_6 4z$  Ⓗ $2\log_6 x + \log_6 y - 4\log_6 z$
  Ⓖ $2\log_6 x \cdot \log_6 y \div 4\log_6 z$  Ⓘ $2\log_6 xy + 4\log_6 z$

**Short Response**

11. For the years 2000–2005, the median price of a single-family home in the United States can be approximated by the exponential function $A = 227,200(1.087)^t$, where $t$ is the number of years after the year 2000.

  a. What is the growth rate of housing prices for this period?

  b. What was the median price of a single-family home in the year 2005?

  a. 8.7%, b. $344,791.10

12. Order the expressions below from least to greatest. Show your work.

  $5^2$    $\log_5 2$    $2^5$    $\log_2 5$    $\log 5$

  $5^2 = 25$, $\log_5 2 \approx 0.43$, $2^5 = 32$, $\log_2 5 \approx 2.32$, $\log 5 \approx 0.70$; $\log_5 2$, $\log 5$, $\log_2 5$, $5^2$, $2^5$

13. Solve the inequality $|2x + 2| > 4$. Graph the solution.

  $x < -3$ or $x > 1$

  ◄—●———————●—► 
  $-4 \ -3 \ -2 \ -1 \ \ 0 \ \ 1 \ \ 2 \ \ 3$

**Extended Response**

14. You and your friend are saving for college. You have $50 and are adding $10 each week to your savings. Your friend has $20 and he is adding $20 each week to his savings.

  a. What system of equations would be a good model for this situation? Let $x$ be number of weeks and $y$ be the number of dollars saved.

  b. Graph your system of equations.

  c. Use your graph to determine when you and your friend will have the same amount of money saved. Explain your answer.

[4] a. $\begin{cases} y = 10x + 50 \\ y = 20x + 20 \end{cases}$

  c. 3 weeks; $y = 10x + 50$ and $y = 20x + 20$ intersect at $(3, 80)$.

[3] appropriate equations and correct graph, but with error in reading the solution from the point of intersection of the system of equations

[2] incorrect equations or graphical errors in evaluating the solution to the system of equations

[1] correct system of equations and graphs, without work shown

[0] incorrect answers and no work shown OR no answers given

## page 73

### Chapter 7 Project Teacher Notes: Crime Time

**About the Project**

The Chapter Project gives students the opportunity to explore how mathematics is used in forensic science. Students investigate the validity of the alibi of a suspect of a crime by using Newton's Law of Cooling. They verify formulas by using natural logarithms to solve equations. Students use these equations to calculate information that will help them prove or disprove the suspect's alibi. They present their conclusions in an investigative report.

**Introducing the Project**

- Ask students if they are familiar with the field of forensic science.
- Discuss information that can help indict a crime suspect.
- Have students review direct variation.

**Activity 1: Investigating**

Students consider information that can help prove or disprove a crime suspect's alibi.

**Activity 2: Writing**

Students use direct variation to write an equation for Newton's Law of Cooling.

**Activity 3: Solving**

Students use natural logarithms to solve equations.

**Activity 4: Calculating**

Students calculate how long ago a car's engine was running at its normal operating temperature.

**Finishing the Project**

You may wish to plan a project day on which students share their completed projects. Encourage students to explain their processes as well as their results. Ask students to review their project work and update their folders.

- Have students review any information needed in order to be able to prove or disprove the alibi. Have them summarize how they solved the formulas used in the project.
- Ask groups to share their insights that resulted from completing the project, such as any shortcuts they found for solving formulas or for researching information.

## page 74

### Chapter 7 Project: Crime Time

**Beginning the Chapter Project**

Forensic science is the application of science to law. A forensic scientist investigates evidence that can help place a suspect at the scene of a crime. Each piece of forensic evidence may help build a successful case against a suspect in a court of law.

In this project, you will examine how mathematics can be used by forensic scientists to help indict people suspected of criminal actions.

**List of Materials**

- Calculator

**Activities**

**Activity 1: Investigating**

A major crime occurred at approximately 10:15 P.M. Shortly thereafter, a certain make and model car, along with its license plate number, were recorded by a witness who reportedly had seen the car speeding in the vicinity of the crime scene. Police and forensic scientists immediately went to the home of the person to whom the car was registered, where they found the car parked in the driveway. The investigation team noted that it had taken them 30 minutes to travel to the suspect's home from the crime scene. They also noted that the engine of the car was still warm when they arrived at 11:00 P.M. When confronted, the suspect claimed to have been at a friend's house earlier that night and had returned home at about 10:00 P.M. The suspect's friend confirmed the alibi, and reported calling the suspect at home at about 10:00 P.M., and having a conversation with the suspect until about 10:20 P.M. What information can investigators use to help prove or disprove the suspect's alibi? Explain. Check students' work.

**Activity 2: Writing**

As police questioned the suspect, the team of forensic scientists began to take temperature measurements of the vehicle's engine coolant, knowing that this information could help determine how long it had been since the engine had been running. In order to determine this time, forensic scientists use Newton's Law of Cooling. This law states that the change in temperature of an object over time $t$, denoted $T'$, varies directly with the difference between the temperature of the object $T$ and the temperature of the surrounding environment, or ambient temperature, $A$. Letting $-k$ represent the constant of variation for a positive value of $k$, write an equation to represent Newton's Law of Cooling. $T' = -k(T - A)$

## page 75

### Chapter 7 Project: Crime Time (continued)

**Activity 3: Solving**

Using calculus and the equation you wrote in Activity 2, the team determined that the temperature of an object after time $t$ in minutes is given by the formula $T(t) = A + (T_0 - A)e^{-kt}$, where $T_0$ represents the temperature at time $t = 0$. Verify that the constant of variation can be found by using the formula $k = -\frac{1}{t_1}\ln\left(\frac{T_1 - A}{T_0 - A}\right)$, where $T_1$ represents the temperature at some later time $t_1$. Then, verify that $t_n$, the time the engine stopped running at a normal operating temperature, is given by $t_n = -\frac{1}{k}\ln\left(\frac{T_n - A}{T_0 - A}\right)$, where $T_n$ represents the normal operating temperature of the engine.

$T(t) = A + (T_0 - A)e^{-kt}$                    $T(t) = A + (T_0 - A)e^{-kt}$

$T_1 = A + (T_0 - A)e^{-kt_1}$                   $T_n = A + (T_0 - A)e^{-kt_n}$

$T_1 - A = (T_0 - A)e^{-kt_1}$                   $T_n - A = (T_0 - A)e^{-kt_n}$

$\frac{T_1 - A}{T_0 - A} = e^{-kt_1}$            $\frac{T_n - A}{T_0 - A} = e^{-kt_n}$

$\ln\left(\frac{T_1 - A}{T_0 - A}\right) = -kt_1$   $\ln\left(\frac{T_n - A}{T_0 - A}\right) = -kt_n$

$-\frac{1}{t_1}\ln\left(\frac{T_1 - A}{T_0 - A}\right) = k$   $-\frac{1}{k}\ln\left(\frac{T_n - A}{T_0 - A}\right) = t_n$

**Activity 4: Calculating**

When the team began investigating at 11:00 P.M., the initial temperature of the engine's coolant was 150°F. By 11:10 P.M. the temperature had dropped to 130°F. The ambient temperature was 70°F. The normal running temperature of the car's engine, based on its make and model, is about 200°F. Let $t = 0$ represent 11:00 P.M.

- Using this information and the equations from Activity 3, first determine the value of $k$, then determine the value of $t_n$. What does this information tell you? Explain.
- If the suspect's car had been turned off at 10:00 P.M., what would the temperature reading have been at 11:00 P.M.? $k \approx 0.029$; $t_n \approx -16.9$ min; The engine stopped running at its normal operating temperature about 17 min before 11:00 P.M., or at about 10:43 P.M. The suspect could have been in the area around the time the crime occurred; about 93°F

**Finishing the Project**

The activities should help you complete your project. Prepare a presentation in the form of an investigative report, providing evidence that will help clear or indict the suspect. Present your report to your classmates. Then discuss the data that helped you to reach your conclusion(s).

**Reflect and Revise**

Ask a small group of classmates to review your report. Is your information presented clearly? Have you sufficiently explained why the evidence helps to prove or disprove the suspect's alibi? Make any necessary changes and improvements before presenting your project to the class.

**Extending the Project**

Discuss other evidence that an investigator could use to place a suspect at a crime scene. Research how mathematics can be applied to other crime scene evidence. If possible, interview a forensic scientist.

## page 76

### Chapter 7 Project Manager: Crime Time

**Getting Started**

Read the project. As you work on the project, you will need a calculator and materials on which you can record your calculations. Keep all of your work for the project in a folder.

| Checklist | Suggestions |
|---|---|
| ☐ Activity 1: analyzing information | ☐ Consider all the given times and the time of the alleged phone call. |
| ☐ Activity 2: using Newton's Law of Cooling | ☐ Review direct variation (Lesson 2-2). |
| ☐ Activity 3: verifying formulas | ☐ Use $(t_1, T_1)$ in the temperature equation to solve for $k$. Then, use $(t_n, T_n)$ in the temperature equation to solve for $t_n$. |
| ☐ Activity 4: using formulas | ☐ Identify $t_1$, $T_0$, $T_1$, and $A$. Then, identify $T_n$. |

**Scoring Rubric**

**4** Calculations and equations are correct. Explanations are thorough, clear, and well thought out. The investigative report is well organized and presents the information in a logical manner.

**3** Calculations and equations are mostly correct with some minor errors. Explanations are mostly accurate and complete. The investigative report is not well organized.

**2** Calculations and equations contain both minor and major errors. Explanations and the investigative report are incomplete or inaccurate.

**1** Major concepts are misunderstood. Project satisfies few of the requirements and shows poor organization and effort.

**0** Major elements of the project are incomplete or missing.

**Your Evaluation of Project** Evaluate your work, based on the *Scoring Rubric*.

**Teacher's Evaluation of the Project**